The Last Good Year

NEW WRITING SCOTLAND 38

Edited by
Rachelle Atalla
and
Samuel Tongue

Gaelic editor:
Maggie Rabatski

Association for Scottish Literary Studies

Association for Scottish Literary Studies
Scottish Literature, 7 University Gardens
University of Glasgow, Glasgow G12 8QH
www.asls.org.uk

ASLS is a registered charity no. SC006535

First published 2020

British Library Cataloguing in Publication Data

A CIP record for this book is available
from the British Library

ISBN 978-1-906841-42-3

The Association for Scottish Literary Studies
acknowledges the support of Creative Scotland
towards the publication of this book

Typeset in Minion by ASLS
Printed by Bell & Bain Ltd, Glasgow

CONTENTS

INTRODUCTION

Lockdown. Social Distancing. Furlough. Stay Home/Protect the NHS/Save Lives. PPE. #ClapforCarers. Viral Load. Support Bubble. Zoom. Barnard Castle. Test-and-Trace. When the pieces collected here were written and submitted, SARS-CoV-2 was an unknown coronavirus, limited to mammal hosts such as bats or pangolins in isolated jungle areas. However, we now know it did not remain there; it made the zoonotic jump to humans, travelling along the trade routes of our interconnected, globalised world with devasting consequences.

Although the phraseology and new vocabulary of coronavirus does not appear in the current volume, the human concerns that are currently shaping our responses are present: fear, love, anger, and the fragility of the connections we make with one another and the environments in which we find ourselves. Sharon Gunason Pottinger's poem 'Waltzing with Morpheus' imagines the terminal lockdown of long illness; Larry Butler's short piece is a last text to the Glasgow poet and writer Tom Leonard. Both demonstrate that the urgent need to reach out and connect with our loved ones, to hold them when we cannot, nay *should not*, is overwhelming. One of the cruellest aspects of the pandemic has been the essential distance we must take from one another. German Chancellor Angela Merkel summed up the paradox early on in the pandemic: 'Im Moment ist nur Abstand Ausdruck von Fürsorge' – 'for the moment, you show you care by keeping your distance.'

Great writing is able to overcome distance. That first distance, between a reader and the text's created world, is bridged by empathetic language and imagery, an invitation to cross over and out of one's present situation. And this imaginative leap has become ever more important when we are confined, for the most part, behind our front doors. The pieces that Rachelle and I have selected here (from over 700 submissions) helped us make this leap, taking us out of ourselves but, importantly, opening us to those perspectives missing from our reduced purviews. Simon Brown and Samantha Walton imagine societies with a fantastic edge which are nonetheless resonant with our own realities; Olga Wojtas's comic short story blends absurdity with a poignant tone; Dean Atta's sharp poem plays on father-son relations; and Jeda Pearl's poem beautifully highlights how a simple object can cultivate a multitude of emotions.

This is the first *New Writing Scotland* of the new decade and it is a difficult time to take stock of the decade just gone and imagine some of ways in which the next will unfold. For *NWS* to remain a snapshot of the literature written in the ongoing project of a contemporary, progressive, diverse, and vibrant Scotland, there is, as ever, hard work to be done. The way coronavirus has impacted on society has, again, highlighted the faultlines of our racialised systems, with people from Black and Ethnic Minority backgrounds made more vulnerable to the disease through racial inequalities in health, education, housing, and employment. The NHS nurses, doctors, and hospital staff that have contracted Covid-19 and died on the frontlines have been disproportionately from ethnic minorities. As Gary Younge notes, this is what systemic discrimination looks like: 'Not isolated incidents but a range of processes built on presumption, assumption, confidence, ignorance and exclusory institutional, personal and professional networks all buttressed by the dead weight of privilege.'[1] This is just one major example of the systemic racism that plagues our society. Younge goes on to analyse the 'connective tissue' between high levels of mortality amongst ethnic minorities due to Covid-19 and the brutal murder of George Floyd by a policeman from the Minneapolis Police Department. Racial discrimination is a terrifying pandemic that runs throughout the structures of our economic, political, and social lives.

With all this in mind, the work of the Scottish BAME Network of Writers continues to be instrumental in highlighting what needs to be done for the literary sector to be truly inclusive of diverse

---

1   Gary Younge, 'We Can't Breathe', *New Statesman*. 3 June 2020.

voices. The newly formed Black Writers' Guild is also a powerful force for racial justice; as publisher Sharmaine Lovegrove explains: 'We want to help guide our industry to become leading lights in the global movement for racial equality.'[2] It behoves all of us to respond – as readers, writers, editors, programmers, publishers, organisers – with whatever leverage we can usefully apply for change. Rachelle and I worked hard in curating this current selection to provide a multiplicity of genres, styles, and perspectives but we hope that it will encourage even more writers of colour to submit their work here. In light of this open, intersectional stance, I also hope that *New Writing Scotland* can continue to provide a home for and promote Scottish LGBTQI+ writers, especially Trans writers who are one of the most marginalised groups in society. Scottish literature is a house with many mansions but some of those mansions need new owners and a total redesign, inside and out. Some need tearing down completely.

No one annual publication can encapsulate and contain all of the potent and important writing that is happening in any given year. I have enjoyed immensely reading the work submitted over the last three years, and it has been a privilege to contribute to this project. This year, new co-editor Rachelle Atalla joined the team and is a joy to work with (even if we could not meet in person for coffee and biscuits!). She, in turn, will welcome a new co-editor for *NWS* 39. The editorial revolving door spins again, and that is a good thing. In the ASLS office, Duncan Jones and Margaret Renton managed superbly in straitened circumstances and I thank them as ever. Krishan Coupland's brilliant short story 'The Last Good Year' became the title for this iteration of *NWS*; in an age of perpetual crisis, each year sometimes feels like the last. However, with every edition of *New Writing Scotland*, and the writers that it showcases, there is always a little more time.

Samuel Tongue

2   Sian Cain, 'Black Writers' Guild calls for sweeping change in UK publishing', *The Guardian*. 15 June 2020.

NEW WRITING SCOTLAND 40:
SUBMISSION INSTRUCTIONS

The fortieth volume of *New Writing Scotland* will be published in summer 2022. Submissions are invited from writers resident in Scotland or Scots by birth, upbringing or inclination. All forms of writing are welcome: autobiography and memoirs; creative responses to events and experiences; drama; graphic artwork (monochrome only); poetry; political and cultural commentary and satire; short fiction; travel writing or any other creative prose may be submitted, but not full-length plays or novels, though self-contained extracts are acceptable. The work must not be previously published or accepted for publication elsewhere, and may be in any of the languages of Scotland.

Submissions should be uploaded, for free, via Submittable:

nws.submittable.com/submit

Prose pieces should be double-spaced and carry an approximate word-count. Please do not put your name on your submission; instead, please provide your name and contact details, including email and postal addresses, on a covering letter. If you are sending more than one piece, please group everything into one document. **Please send no more than four poems, or one prose work.**

Authors retain all rights to their work(s), and are free to submit and/or publish the same work(s) elsewhere after they appear in *New Writing Scotland*. Successful contributors will be paid at a rate of £20 per published page.

Please be aware that we have limited space in each edition, and therefore shorter pieces are more suitable – although longer items of exceptional quality may still be included. Our maximum suggested word-count is 3,500 words.

Patricia Ace
HIGHLAND FLING

He took me somewhere
no-one would know us,
a hotel at the end of the line.

He told me that navvies
had floated the rails
on a mattress of brash;

a thousand tonnes of soil
and ashes, to stop the bog
from swallowing the tracks.

The hush of the lobby
drove me reckless,
like breaking and entering

the home of a stranger or
looting a stove-in shop.
I caressed the fake flowers,

probing their creases for dust.
Upstairs, in the chintzy bedroom,
I wrestled the bathrobe

from its headless hanger,
left my grubby pants on the floor.
I wore the backless black dress

down to dinner and ate
everything served on my plate.
Have you no shame?

was the question he asked me.
I cannot recall my reply.
Just that it never gets dark

in the Scottish midsummer;
the boyish face of the maître d',
so pale and so eager to please.

Arthur Allen
ON CRATERS

Plate VI.

[dark cuff, palm down   [inverted, wizened
deeply lined, and well known   stalk down
to resemble archipelagos]   sense of abbot
                                                          tonsured planetary]

BACK of HAND   &   SHRIVELLED APPLE.

TO ILLUSTRATE the ORIGIN of CERTAIN MOUNTAIN RANGES
BY SHRINKAGE of the GLOBE

J. Nasmyth   *Heliotype*

James Nasmyth, Edinburgh-born astronomer and entrepreneurial engineer, retired in 1856 at the age of forty-nine to observe the moon. This began his second working life, culminating in the publication of *The Moon: Considered as a Planet, a World, and a Satellite* (1874), co-authored with the astronomer James Carpenter, which ran to four print runs. Work, here, means sketching the mountainous surface of the moon through a twenty-inch reflector telescope, which Nasmyth designed himself and mounted on a turntable. From these minutely detailed drawings he built exact plaster models – extraordinary local maps of the lunar surface – peaks and chasms, rosace craters – and then photographed them for verity of contrast against black backgrounds in sunlight.

Having already invented the steam hammer, Nasmyth had become delicate and scrutinous towards the changing mask of worlds, and he attended with his models to 'the peculiar conditions which would attend a sojourn on the lunar surface.' All moonly questions were open at this time, but Nasmyth was addressing one question in particular: how the formation of the features of the moon could be read [like palimpsest] from its fissures. He suggested that as the lunar sphere cooled and solidified it also expanded, thus forming its characteristic hollows, mountain ranges, chasms and radiating veins. (To demonstrate the emergence of such scores, he provides a photograph of a glass sphere cracked radially by pressure from within.) The most striking illustration, however, is not of the lunar surface itself, or more accurately, of the plaster models Nasmyth built to represent it, but a proof in duplicate that the retraction of natural skin reveals mountains.

Dean Atta
MY DAD'S DICK

after Wayne Holloway-Smith

imagine it
afro-proud   or stoned and slouching
watching a movie

or pointing any which way   it pleases
swinging around
alone in roundwood park at night

or sending angry emails i do not reply to
or making unreasonable requests
or making comments   about my dick

how i call my jizz poetry and they pay me for it
but my dad's dick fills sock after sock
with his jizz

i
his sperm   now published man
imagine it   his dick in my hand

Evgenia Jen Baranova
PARADISE

When she was dying, there was so much food.
They'd brought a chicken pie,
onions and radishes.
She'd received cucumbers, cabbage, wine.
The cucumbers went bad of course, the wine turned sour.
Her brother-in-law
dropped by in the morning, he prayed aloud.
'Are you going to sell your cow now?' he asked.
'We've been waiting for Zirka for so long.'
A thick shawl curled up and slept in the corner,
and the bed smelled of the frosty shawl.
March was going by; the wind drove geese inside,
The geese hissed and honked, got filthy,
crashed against the door.
Stepan and Yevsey used to pray for old women in her time.
Now Arkady, Kirill, and Valeriy pray.
Someone would be lucky if she sold the hut.
What's the use of the saltshaker, tongs, or a ladle now?
When she was dying, it got so light:
the light from the paradise was oozing down
directly onto her windowsill.

(translated from the Russian by Sergey Gerasimov)

Jack Bigglestone
HOW YOU LIKE IT

another wild boy
pinioned
to the old oak
painting up to the tender
edges
of his pain
pricks   the canvas fray
worry   the muscular knot
bachelor nightingales
in the branches   overhead
singing funny valentines
( ) ( ) ( )
i saw a slip at the waist
(you raised those roped arms)
the belt   &   the shirt
and the thrill inbetween
( ) ( ) ( )
a tale passed around
of
a bona cosy cottage
pretty men all in a row
silence   humming
off the damp white tiles
( ) ( ) ( )
our eyes meet through the page's glorious holes
tell me
without moving your mouth
( ) ( ) ( )
alluding softly
under open windows

    laying a trail of
      sugar
          along the strongest boughs
              the gate unlatched

Simon Brown

A BIRD YOU DON'T HAVE TO FEED

The monsoon brings us closer together. When the rain starts I throw up my hood and Dzifa flies in and perches on my neck, so close I feel her heartbeat against my cheek. We stare out at the curtain of rain, thick with the blue and pink lights of the city beyond, then Dzifa nudges me and I open my mouth and she gets to work, shivering after each hot blast of breath. It's true you're not supposed to feed them beyond the mouth pickings but everyone knows it's the first thing a prospective partner checks so I slip her food on the sly. Doesn't do to have some dull, scrawny bird flapping around you, even if you can barely spare the crumbs, even if it's been years since a woman looked at you with anything more than passing interest. The bird is the person.

Dzifa though, she can charm anyone. She's the reason I have so many regulars. Certainly isn't the food. She chirps pleasantly at everyone as they step up to the cart, rubs her little face against theirs while they order and does backflips in the air as they leave. Sometimes she'll get a flock going and they'll tumble together for a while, darting in and out of the holes in the awnings above.

It's why I'm not surprised when, during a break in the downpour, some well-heeled woman, who one of my neighbours tells me is a politician, comes sloshing through the groundwater towards my stall, a legion of photographers and bodyguards in tow. I keep my eyes low, study the rainbow patterns that spilt cooking oil and spicedust create in the puddles.

'I hear you make the best bofrot in town,' she says. When she smiles the cameras chirrup in unison.

'Not true,' I say. 'You want to try Kwame down the other end.' Her bird lands on her shoulder and cocks its head. 'His are better.'

She touches my arm and throws back her head and laughs, eliciting another bout of chirruping from the cameras. So fake. But as she does this her bird copies her, even going as far as

making a trilling, cascading noise that sounds eerily like laughter.
I smile.

'You don't encounter humility too often as a politician,' she says.
'Very refreshing. Now how about you get cooking?'

I do what I'm told, grateful that she asks me to make some for
the bodyguards and photographers too, even if it is a pretty naked
attempt at winning them over. It's all muscle memory, so I can tune
out of the process and pay attention to what's going on around me.
Other street vendors peer over the photographers' shoulders, faces
taut with envy as the politician fields questions about how often
she eats street food ('all the time, it's a guilty pleasure'). But that
doesn't interest me because I'm watching our birds.

Dzifa is acting strange. Coy. Practically tucking her beak behind
a wing. This other bird, whose name I find out is Asare, hops
around her, crooning like an old gondolier. I don't know that I've
ever seen romance between two animals before. Warms my heart.
But I can't dwell on them for too long as the bofrot are ready and
I need to start handing them out.

The politician takes a big mouthful and then an even bigger
bite of the scenery as she doubles over, buckled by the taste
sensation.

She points a finger to the bofrot. 'Amazing,' she says. We pose
for some photos and she's about to head on her way – though she
still hasn't eaten more than that first mouthful – when the rain
begins to lash down again, like something in the sky has burst.
Hood up, I scramble to cover everything and run for the nearest
complete piece of awning. So does the politician. Her two bodyguards are forced to stand in the downpour but if it bothers them
they don't show it. One yawns and a little pair of eyes peek out
from inside his mouth. The politician flashes me a quick smile and
pulls out her phone. I get it. The rain pounds on the fabric above
us, then a long, slow peal of thunder rolls in like a half-speed
crash cymbal. You can smell the electricity in the air.

Something's wrong. My neck feels lighter. Dzifa hasn't come in to roost. I straighten and hurriedly scan the market, sweat already bubbling all over my body. I'm missing an arm or minus a kidney. An image of the shadow people, birdless and bereft, flashes across my mind before a crack of lightning scours it away and fills the whole market with a brilliant white light.

That's when I spot her. She and Asare are nestled under a part of the cover that spills over my cookware, creating a natural canopy. Her head is buried into his breast. My heart bucks to see this. I nudge the politician. She scowls at my intrusion but as soon as she claps eyes on those two this expression melts away.

'Cute,' she says, half-smiling, before sticking her head back in her phone.

Soon the rain's eased off and while people emerge and pick up their bustle the politician pockets her phone and whistles for Asare.

He doesn't move.

I stop what I'm doing, glance about to see if there are any other witnesses, making sure I keep my face blank. This is unprecedented. Even I haven't had my bird ignore me and I'm the lowest of the low.

The politician's cheek twitches and she slops through the mud to where Dzifa and Asare are nestled into one another.

'Asare,' she says, each syllable spiked with barbed wire. He glances at her and his head drops. The two birds chirp mournfully, tremulously. Asare sticks his beak into his plumage and produces a single feather which he lays at Dzifa's feet, then returns to the politician and her hissed remonstrations. He sits backwards on her shoulder as the two leave, repeating a single chirp that slides downwards in pitch.

She's quiet the rest of the day, is Dzifa, and not even small bits of bofrot – a rare treat – can coax back her lustre. Once we're home she sits by the window with Asare's feather in front of her, staring wistfully out at the neon pink clouds that smother the city. During my evening groom her sighs echo around my mouth and when I shuffle off to bed she's still looking out at the city. It busts me, seeing this, and I'm up most of the night, trying to shake the thoughts from my head. By morning I've made my decision. There will be consequences but who am I to stand in the way of love? If one of us has a shot at happiness then we should surely take it.

She perks up as soon as she realises we're not heading to the market. The bus trundles up expansive, gleaming streets and I feel more and more uncomfortable in my frayed and faded clothes. The thought flashes across my mind that maybe they'll think it's chic, that maybe this middle-aged woman with all her extraneous flesh is at the cutting edge of something, but I know as soon as I think it that this is a ridiculous thought.

I traipse up the road towards parliament house, with its luminous green lawn peppered with sprinklers and rainbows, and the closer we get the more animated Dzifa becomes. The sun has barely begun to peek over the horizon so we wait.

She shows up a couple of hours later and would have managed to completely avoid me if it hadn't been for Asare zipping over and swirling around us.

'You . . .' she begins once she's come over, eyebrows knotted from the effort of recalling where she knows my face from.

'You visited my bofrot stand yesterday.' I tilt my head at the two birds, who are swirling around in the air together, caught in a private tornado. 'Was Asare himself last night?'

The politician takes a step back and her face softens. 'No.'

'Neither was Dzifa. Seems we have a couple of lovebirds here.'

The softness vanishes. 'Listen, if it's money you want you've co—'

I wave a hand. 'I don't want money. I want you to take her.'

'Oh.' She pauses a moment, weighing up the political hay she could make out of having two birds instead of one. 'That could work.'

My heart lurches. Some tiny part of me hoped she'd say no so I wouldn't have to go through with this. I call Dzifa and have her land on my finger.

'I want you to go with her,' I say, speaking slowly to keep my voice from cracking. 'I want you to be with Asare.' I never know how much she understands but I tell her 'I'll miss you' anyway.

She stares at me, head cocked as if she's not quite willing to believe what I've said, so I put my finger next to the politician's shoulder and nudge her on. I can't cry because if I do then she might not go.

'Are you sure about this?' asks the politician, stroking Dzifa's head. 'You know what happens now.'

I shrug. 'One of us deserves to be happy.'

I leave, stumbling because of the tears that smear my vision, but before I've gone very far Dzifa flutters around me, chirping an upbeat, frenetic tune crammed with notes.

'You're welcome,' I say.

*

It all happens so quickly. Customers avoid my stand. Neighbours ignore me in the stairs. Buses drive past me. The few social inter-actions I manage to wheedle out of people are tense, like the other person's being held at gunpoint. I try and stay outside all day, just in case a passing free bird decides it wants to roost with me, but of course it doesn't happen. Never will.

I get home on the first evening without Dzifa to find the locks have been changed. A stranger answers the door, all smiles until he notices I'm missing a bird.

'Don't know what to tell you, ma'am,' he says stiffly. 'We've always lived here.'

'Bullshit. I see boxes. You haven't even unpacked yet.'

He pushes me away. 'You so much as breathe on this door again and I'll call the cops.'

He slams the door in my face and I start pounding it. 'Hey. *Hey!* I want my things.'

No one comes to the door despite all that pounding, but it turns out he wasn't bluffing about calling the police. Two officers come loping up the stairs, their birds and handsets bleeping and warbling in unison.

'There a problem?' says the larger of the two, whose thin side-burns look like insect legs.

'Squatters,' I say. 'They've changed the locks and everything.'

The officer makes a show of looking around the landing. 'Where's your bird?'

I sigh. 'I'm between birds at the moment.'

He grabs my arm and digs his fingertips deep into the muscle. 'Then you can't be here.'

'Where the hell am I supposed to go?'

The large officer grins at his colleague. 'Oh we'll show you.'

*

After the beating they leave me in the gutter, where I watch my blood mingle with mud and wait for the world to stop spinning. Some time later, a hand gently rocks my shoulder. I turn over. A woman with worn but kind eyes says hello, that she saw everything, that they've all been there at some point.

'Who's we?'

Even as I ask, the scaffolding clinging to the sides of the buildings comes into focus, as do the scores of shadowy figures staring over its edges.

*

'I guess I told myself you were made up,' I say once I'm back on my feet and climbing gingerly up the ladder to the first level of scaffolding. The wood beneath my fingers is soft and bits come away in my hand.

'People train themselves to ignore us,' she says. 'But we're here. Clinging to the sides of civilisation. Surviving.'

Up on the first level, people are busy making fake birds. Some glue taxidermied plovers to their shoulders, others opt for photos stuck to cardboard. None are convincing.

'They're all new,' says the woman. 'Still playing by society's rules, however bastardised. Let's keep going.'

As we rise through the levels the number of people fooling around with fake birds dwindles. Here rats and mice scamper over people's shoulders as they read, play cards or chat. They seem happy enough but when they smile their teeth are black.

'Higher,' says the woman.

By the time we reach the upper levels there are no animals to be seen, alive or otherwise. The woman shows me her plank of wood. We're so high up that when she sits she looks like she's resting on a carpet of cloud. Behind her, somewhere over the sea, the sun's fading rays tease out the most fragile of rainbows.

'What do you do up here?'

The woman smiles. Her teeth are white. 'Up here we know that we don't need animals clinging to us all the time. We're happy as we are. Do you know there are some societies which don't use birds at all?'

My eyes widen. 'Really? How do they keep things clean?'

The woman takes something out of her pocket and holds it out reverentially.

'What is it?'

'It's called a "toothbrush".'

I mouth the word myself, just to try it out.

'You stick it in your mouth like *so*, then move it around to clear things out. It's sort of like a bird you don't have to feed.'

'How strange.'

'The point is,' she says, slipping the toothbrush carefully back into her pocket, 'you don't have to play by their rules.'

I edge towards the ladder, smiling politely. This kind of thinking might be contagious. 'Thanks for rescuing me. I might try and find myself another bird all the same.'

'Once they're gone, they're gone. You know that.'

'We'll see,' I say as I start climbing down.

The woman laughs and shakes her head. 'See you when you're ready.'

I return to the first level. You won't catch me sticking some cheap bit of plastic in my mouth, that's for damn sure. We have traditions for a reason. I cadge a stuffed plover off someone heading up to the second level and begin gluing it to my shoulder.

Larry Butler
LAST TEXT TO TOM LEONARD

YumYum and Latte 3pm at your house. Text me if you prefer
      something else
Larry

Angela T. Carr

SONG OF THE KINGSTON BRIDGE OVERPASS, 2 A.M.

Glasgow (1993)

Out the club's thumping blackness, we stumble
into the sodium flicker of rain-slicked streets, glowing

from the heave of the dancefloor, clothes clung to torso,
wedged in crotch, our carefully constructed faces

sliding from the anchors of brows and lids,
our bodies' heat turning to steam in the night's cut,

push past the squall on the street, fist fights, deflated faces
streaked in tears, drunk and stung by hormones and
        rejection,

the quietly desperate who, earlier, necked pints and shots
        and slumped
to the toilet cubicle floor, as queues of bladder-pressed girls

wriggled, fixed their hair, squinting in mirrors, flat-palmed
banging on the door: *'C'mon tae fuck, I'm burstin' oot here!'*

now, squatting on pavement kerbs, counselled and cajoled:
'Yer better aff wi'oot him, the bastert! Fuck 'im, anyways,'

and we trip on, past the doxie, skirt hitched, peeing in a
        doorway,
the dark stream of her leading us down the street, as we're
        called

to the petrol-singe of burgers, the spitting song of the
       hotplate
from the mobile chip van and the motorway roaring
       overhead

as we bellow orders, ears still ringing, shouting, *'Salt, aye.*
Naw, nae vinegar,' then run to catch the late-night bus

where, greasy-pawed, our mouths oily 'O's, we tumble
into each other at last, suck the darkness from salt-crusted
       lips.

Krishan Coupland
THE LAST GOOD YEAR

January

Cold month. There's plenty of work selling pills in winter. Flu capsules and sore throat tablets. Organic remedies are big this year: little foil-wrapped powder kegs of chalk and sugar. Placebos, all of them. Brian tries a few himself, lying on his too-big hotel-room bed, popping the tabs and sucking or swallowing or chewing as appropriate. He's been ill since late last year; a stubborn cold that just won't shift. The pills don't stop his nose from running, but they make him feel charged, confident. When it gets too dark to read the foils he reaches for the phone.

'Kelly? It's Brian. From the bar?'

They sit in his room until three a.m. He orders vodka and sandwiches from room service, and tips the boy who brings them, and makes sure she sees him do it. He tells her about his wife, his beautiful son. About his house with a view of the ocean. He tells her that there's no cure for the common cold. That there's nothing you can do for it except mitigate the symptoms.

February

He returns around midday to an empty house. He drops his travel case and sample box in the hall and walks about, paging through weeks-old post. The dog – an ageing Labrador, long-since deaf – is asleep in its basket in the kitchen, whining softly with each inward breath. It is a Monday and he thought that Jane would be home. He'd imagined a dozen times the look of surprise that would break across her face. How they'd hug. How he would carry her to the bedroom . . .

She'll arrive back later, no doubt, with Sam and the shopping.

Until then he sits in the armchair and watches TV. Before he knows it he's asleep, and then when he wakes it is to Jane standing before him, shrugging off her handbag.

'Hey.' He's so sleepy that his brain isn't working. 'I'm back.'

She stares at him for a minute without saying anything. She looks as if she's put on weight. Her lips, pressed thin, look bright in the middle of her wheat-coloured face. 'You didn't tell me you'd be early,' she says, and there's no delight or surprise in her voice. She's merely stating facts, noting inconsistencies, bland and procedural as a police officer.

There is a crash, and Sam enters like a storm, crying already. He's at an age where his every other utterance is a scream or tears. Where his misery and his loudness are never-ending. It often seems to Brian disproportionate in someone so small – all that bottomless rage. Today, distraught over something that Brian cannot comprehend, he has kicked over Brian's sample box and sent a thousand gaudy sugar pills skittering across the floor.

March

He takes the dog for a walk on the beach. Throws sticks for it and watches it chase up through the surf bounding and barking. It's getting dark and the beach is empty. The foam froths ice-white and sinks into the sand. Looking back Brian can see his house, perched up on top of the cliff like a lonely tooth. When Sam was very little they called it the Lighthouse Cottage, but they don't say that anymore.

The dog comes panting back to him, stick in mouth, turning in excited circles. Brian takes the stick and throws it, then wipes his hand on his jeans. He wipes his nose as well, which is running freely in the cold. He always experiences this feeling of *off*ness whenever he returns from London. It's the kind of thing he imagines astronauts feel when their capsule first enters gravity. Seeping heaviness. Sluggishness. No longer is he floating weightless from hotel room to conference venue. He is here, surrounded by things that should make him feel safe and comforted. And none of it does. Instead it all just feels slightly sickly. A complex, uncomfortable, loud existence over which he has not the slightest bit of control.

The dog returns, stick in mouth, its black body coated with particles of sand. He takes the wet piece of wood and hurls it once more towards the surf. He looks back to the house. Raises his thumb and squints along the length of his arm, obscuring the house completely. Everything he owns in the entire world can be found in that tiny white sugar cube, already almost lost to the dark.

April

She's there before him, sipping coffee and reading a book which she shuts and slips away into her handbag before he can catch the title. How young she is, and how graceful. Every movement could belong to an actress. She's wearing a dress and a leather jacket, her hair neatly bunched. She smiles, pretty as ever, and he feels his stomach move in a way that it hasn't for seven years.

'What are you reading?' he says.

'*The Hitchhiker's Guide.*'

'You like it?'

She smiles. She tells him about tai chi. She joined six weeks ago and it's the best thing she's ever done. It makes her feel like her insides have been removed, rinsed clean and replaced, dripping soapy water. In summer months they practice in the park and people stop to watch them moving in eerie symphony. He imagines her stretching, cool silent movements like a monk or a dancer. She tells him about her last boyfriend, his ownership issues. She's so *tired* of younger men.

Brian sips his coffee. His throat is dry: that same stubborn cold that won't quite shift.

May

She meets him at the hotel. Kisses him on the mouth as soon as he shuts the door. The first time is better than Brian has had in years. So is the second. And the third. While she showers he calls home and leaves a message for Jane: *Arrived okay. Weather awful. Miss you. First meeting at nine tomorrow.* He puts the phone down and lies flat. His hips and shoulders ache hotly from moving in ways they've not needed to before. He rolls over, opens the sample box and digs out a roll of painkillers, popping two that fizz and dissolve to nothing on his tongue. The thing with painkillers, he reflects, is that you don't feel anything. Easy to see why, when people decide to overdose, they do so on them.

Kelly emerges, one towel wrapped around her body and another around her hair. She kneels above him on the bed, wet and warm and soft. A droplet trembles at the tip of a stray strand of hair, then falls to his chest. For the rest of the evening he doesn't think about home at all.

June

There's another visit from the council. Two men this time, both neatly dressed and overweight in the comfortable, self-contained way that bureaucrats often are. Jane makes them tea and Brian sits through the usual set of warnings. One of the men has brought a colour diagram of the cliffs which animates like a flick-book. Brian watches as a cartoon house on a cliff is approached by a crumbling edge. Undermined, it tumbles jerkily down onto the rocks below, breaking into white confetti. He takes their leaflets and signs a piece of paper. He says he'll be in touch.

Jane shows them out, then returns and drops into the seat opposite Brian. She picks up a corner of the tablecloth and starts twisting it, tighter and tighter. 'We have to move,' she says.

'We should—'

She shakes her head. 'I don't *care*, Brian. I'm sick of it.' She twists the tablecloth some more, so that the corners pull taut and the salt-shaker falls over. 'Sick of living here. We're going to move, okay? You promise me. We're going to move.'

She stares at the wall behind his head, seeming calm, as though this is nothing more than a chore: mundane and contemptible as the school run. In the next room Sam is watching cartoons, bellowing rage at the television in between comedic bonks and klaxons. And it all seems so worthless – everything that he's drawn around him through years and years and years of work. And he loved her once, he's sure of that. Her and Sam both. How many million pills did he have to sell to afford this house, to build this life? It must have meant something once. It must have been worth saving.

'Okay?' says Jane.

Brian looks at her. Looks at the fallen salt-shaker. He reaches over and stands it back up. 'Okay,' he says.

July

He intends, on seeing her, to tell her that he cannot keep seeing her. He rehearses it as he drives, the exact words that he will use, so that when the time comes he can open his mouth and spool them out without resistance: '*This has gone on long enough . . . I'm a married man . . .*' Words which sound good and strong and noble in his head.

When he lets himself into the hotel room she comes padding out of the bathroom barefoot, pinning up her hair. She smiles. *One last time*, he thinks, as he has thought again and again for weeks now, his thoughts washing up against reality like a weak tide, nothing more in them than scads of froth. He hates her for it. The softness of her young body, its difference. The way she pushes her head back against the pillows. Her curved and suntanned neck.

August

It happens in the middle of the night. Brian wakes and the house is shaking, vibrating like a ringing phone with the friction of earth moving against earth. He sits up and swings his feet out of bed. The shaking stops. Jane sleeps peaceably beside him, her breath even and calm. He goes downstairs, cold feet on cold laminate. Outside the patio doors the saplings bend nearly horizontal in hurricane winds.

The very end of the garden is gone. There's nothing there, where the bean plants and the climbing arch and Jane's stone bench used to be. A section of fencing protrudes over the edge, drooping towards nothingness, the bottom of one post still clayed in earth. Standing here, in the back doorway of his house, he can now see the sea. Brian watches it, the reaching fury flinging itself inland. Then he shuts the door and creeps back up to bed.

In the morning, Sam weeps and stamps his foot, demanding to look over the edge. While Jane is busy talking to the council, Brian takes his son's hand and leads him to the lip of the cliff. The both of them lie down flat on dew-damped grass and crawl forward, peeking down, down, down to the colours on the rocks below. Seeing it for the first time in daylight Brian is struck by the thrill of just how much ground they have lost. He had thought that such a distance would stretch out over years. Decades are sprawled down there on the rocks. It was all never more than rubble anyway.

'Don't be scared,' he says to Sam. He puts a hand on his son's back and feels the heartbeat of his child through thin cotton, through skin and bone. The only time he's touched him in months. The calmest, most docile his son has ever been. For a moment he wonders if it is the sight of destruction that has appeased him. Then Sam bats away his hand.

'Not scared. Not scared of anything.' He scrambles to his feet, still dizzyingly close to the edge, and stamps back towards the house.

September

The council come and put up fencing along the back of the garden. It is the orange, modular kind usually reserved for road workings – not a barrier but another warning. He watches the men who come to install it as they heft the plastic sections into place. It's a warning for him: *There's danger here, just like we've always said there was.*

Finally, after another argument, he and Jane visit an estate agent. They are given tea and coffee, loaded into a minibus and shown around an endless array of houses. All of them are small. None have a view of the ocean. The estate agent tells them that they have to use their imagination, have to see if they can picture themselves living here.

Brian pictures Kelly. Her faraway little flat which he's only visited once; her bicycle mounted on the wall. Pencil-shaded free drawings of Disney characters pinned to the fridge. She would fold into his life like a bookmark. She would sit just there, curled and barefoot on the sofa. Or in the Lighthouse Cottage, wandering hand in hand with him along the beach. Cuddled in bed in the middle of a storm. No Jane. No Sam. He and Kelly, their days repeating, frozen forever, never growing closer nor further away from the white wet roar of the sea.

October

Jane is standing at the sink washing mugs and Brian comes in and puts his arms around her waist. She twitches and drops the cup she's washing so that it smashes in the sink and she turns around and pushes him away leaving two wet and foaming handprints on the front of his jumper.

'Don't *do* that,' she screams. And Brian doesn't know what he's done, and so he turns around and walks out. All the way through the house and out the front door. He gets into the car and drives, not caring where, anywhere, away. His face is hot and red. He can feel his pulse in the lids of his eyes.

'*Don't* do *that.*' As though he'd hit her. Her hurt face and hands still dripping and broken porcelain in the sink. Broken porcelain which she would now be picking up and tipping into the bin. The sound it had made explosive and keen-edged. Three hours later he finds himself in London, outside Kelly's apartment building. He cannot remember which flat is hers and so he tries several buzzers until a voice answers which sounds familiar.

'It's me,' he says. 'Can you let me in? Please.'

A long pause. She lets him in. The bicycle is still there in the hallway, but the walls have been painted. It no longer smells of incense but of air and washed linen.

'Brian.' She greets him from two landings up. 'You should have called.'

'I'm sorry,' he says.

'I'm on my period,' she says. They go through to the bedroom and lie there, holding each other. After an hour or so, clearly thinking him asleep, Kelly disentangles herself and goes back out into the apartment. Brian hears her talking on the phone.

November

When he gets home one evening Jane is sitting on the stairs, face blotchy, looking small and tightly wound. The hall lights are off. Sam is in the other room watching television. Cartoons. A rush of noise and fury filtering through the closed door.

'Well?' she says. And he knows at once that she knows. He opens his mouth, ready to apologise and explain and make everything understood and there is nothing there, no words, nothing ready to be said. Jane's face crumples. He turns around and leaves and he is crying even though he has known for months that this was coming, and it is cold out and he left his coat in the hall. Jane follows him, screaming down the street. If they had neighbours the neighbours would see but there's nobody else out here on the clifftop road and he loves it, the isolation and the ever-roaring sound of the sea and their tiny warm house perfect among everything that can be seen. In the exact moment of losing it, he loves it most of all.

'Who is she?' screams Jane. 'How long?'

It's dark and he cannot see where he's going. A car is approaching, yellow-white headlamps dipping and rising over the bluffs. He moves to the side of the road. Jane catches up with him. He opens his mouth again and feels nothing but air in his throat, wet air that tastes of salt. Instead of the planned apology he says this: 'I want the house. Take Sam. Take anything you want, but I want to keep the house.'

December

He comes home one evening and the post is piled neatly on the hall table. All down the length of the corridor are clean bright squares where pictures used to hang. The television is gone, the sofas now pointing to a cobwebbed corner. The dog doesn't come running to greet him. There is no dog. Sam's room has been stripped completely, all the toys bundled up and taken, nothing left but the felt-tip scribblings that adorn the walls.

He calls Kelly and leaves a message on her phone. She calls him back while he is cooking spaghetti in the kitchen, using a new saucepan with the label still clinging to the handle.

'I can come if you pay my train fare. If I leave right after work I'll get there half seven,' she says.

'Okay,' he says. 'I love you.'

'Okay,' she says.

At half-past seven he drives into town and picks her up from outside the station. At the house they eat reheated spaghetti off brand-new plates and he shows her the broken garden, the ever-creeping invasion of the sea.

'Is it safe?' she asks.

'Of course. The council know.'

They go upstairs. On the bed in which Brian and his wife slept for seven years they have sex. Through the gap in the curtains Brian can see the ocean, the inrushing roll of the waves. Kelly groans, snakes arms around his shoulders, digs nails into the paunchy flesh of his back. He can feel a shudder that runs through everything: the house, the bed, the girl who's not his wife, the orange barriers, the empty bedroom with pen-scribbled walls, the truncated garden, the gleaming kitchen and picture-less hall. Everything he's come to own.

Carol Farrelly
LIKEWISE

Sean didn't want to be on this journey. He didn't want to stand on this deck that struggled while enginemen slowed the pistons below. He gripped the railing tighter and reminded himself this was only a visit. There was no permanence to this return. He'd come to tell them his decision in person, as any decent son and brother would; he'd come to watch them buckle in reply, and stand and bear it, as any grown man should.

'We're almost there,' a voice said behind him.

He lifted his eyes and Dún Laoghaire's harbour curved large around him. The town's hazy outline had thickened and darkened into the familiar landmarks.

'Doesn't it look just the same?' said the voice.

And it was true. There, to the left, stood the hotel's white parliament of windows while there, to the right, the Pavilion's squat roof. Beyond, rose the vying spires of St Michael's and the Mariner's, higher than all the other rooftops.

'Look at the windows, all lit up,' said a woman this time. 'Isn't it a wonder to see lit windows again?'

Sean turned his back to the harbour and the criss-crossing headwinds. He stood and watched as the other passengers crowded the deck and pressed against the railings. Like him, they were returning from their labours in England: some for a visit, and some on a single fare. And they were a typical flock of migrant workers – mostly young, some scrawny, some stout – but all bringing back whatever measures of milk and honey they had made from Ireland's neutrality. Or 'The Emergency' as they called it back here. Most gazed wide-eyed towards the bay, homesick hearts in their mouths, as though they'd been travelling the sea for months. Only a few, like him, looked away.

Every passenger, though, whether glad or loath to return, was putting away England. He could see it in their eyes, the memories

draining. Pack away all England's darkness: the blacked-out
windows; the spindly bunk beds; the shopkeepers and landlords
whose scales and pumps turned suddenly miserly on hearing Irish
vowels; the corrugated tin huts shared with a dozen Englishmen,
gimlet-eyed, who would always sing the praises of their soldier
sons whenever you were in earshot. Pack away England's light too:
the hot, lazy, churchless Sundays; the dance halls that seemed to
glitter saxophones; Mary's silver pendant ticking back and forth
as she moved above him.

Sean let the memory shudder out his bones and then turned to
face the harbour again, just a rope's throw away now. Any moment,
Orla would call out his name and become real again: the little sister
who had written him two years' worth of spidery letters, all tapping
out their Morse-code plea. *Come home, please. Deliver me from
this almighty boredom. Come back.* A message Mam had sounded
out too in her quieter letters. She'd be at home right now, eyeing
the clock, laying the special rose-embroidered tablecloth, sweeten-
ing a rabbit stew, plumping up his pillow for the tenth time. He
knew not to expect Mam amongst the waiting crowd: she'd told
him so in her latest letter. She couldn't bear to see him on that
gangway again, even if he was coming home this time. She'd only
recall the jagged white ticket that had hung from his lapel, number
thirty-four, when he'd left. 'Like a calf marked as veal,' she'd said.

He felt the other reason, though, for her absence. If she saw him
there at the harbour, her bones would feel his decision like a rheu-
matism. Mam had more sense than Orla of how things would have
gone in England. Go home to your coward bed or enlist: that was
the choice every Irishman heard over there. Enough of your prof-
iteering. Never a mention of the centuries they'd ravaged your own
soil. Blinking eyes if you ever referred them to the bloodshed, or
famine, or burnt-down homes. Sean, though, had made his choice
in the end, and he told himself it was the right and honourable
one. Mam would weep when she learned it and Orla would slope
her shoulders and slam doors, but he wouldn't buckle. He wouldn't

sit by lit-up windows, 'while half the world braves the blackout'. He'd use those same words the Englishmen had used on him.

'Sure I've missed this place,' a man said behind him. 'You can't beat your native land, so.'

'Where folk understand you,' said another.

A rag of wind flapped across Sean's face. A seagull yelped and raced across the sky, as though on a wire. A child's sandy, mop-haired head butted his legs. A blonde woman puckered her lipsticked mouth towards a small mirror. He saw her ring finger was bare and wondered if she was just visiting and would return to England. A woman, after all, knew a different world over there: she could stretch out her arms and her fingertips didn't feel walls. She could dance till all hours, skip the weekly confession, watch films untouched by the Irish censor. She could do all those things without hearing the slow roar an Irishman heard. The tolerance thin as dust. *Sign up. Enlist. Go home.* He'd never envied a woman before for freedoms he didn't have.

'Make way!'

The pistons stopped and the deck shuddered. The woman with the mirror stumbled. A hush fell as ropes sprang through the air and coiled onto the pier. Everyone bustled portside and the boat tilted. The fist inside Sean's stomach clenched tighter.

'Make way now!' A white-haired official battened the gangway into place.

Sean looked down. The waiting crowd had faces now. A cold sweat sickened him.

'Johnny!' the woman with the mirror called and all the passengers stared because she was the first to see her loved one.

Sean pushed towards the gangway and a stocky man elbowed him then mumbled an apology. Sean nodded. He'd seen him earlier, when they'd boarded at Holyhead. He'd been wearing a soldier's uniform then, and everyone had kept their distance. At some point, he must have packed the uniform into his rucksack, all neat and taciturn and neutral as de Valera requested. 'Are you glad you

signed?' Sean wanted to ask him. 'And what was your reason?
And does it feel like escape?'

'Sean,' a voice shouted.

Orla stood at the bottom of the shaking steps, waving and
grinning, taller than ever.

Sean started down the gangway.

'And how are you, little sister?' he cried over the heads of
descending passengers.

'Grand,' Orla laughed. 'I'm absolutely grand now.'

Sean slapped his arms around her as he set foot again on
homeland. His stomach cramped. He tried to concentrate on his
sister, this moment of reunion. Her black hair was curled in the
latest fashion, her eyes brilliant blue like a newborn's, her embrace
steady and warm. She felt stronger in arm and shoulder since Sean
had last seen her. All the open-sea swimming she'd described in
her letters had layered muscle into her, but it didn't sit comfortable
yet. Eighteen years old and still she hunched and looked to the
ground, fending off judgements and compliments alike. Sean
wanted both to pull her closer and push her away.

'God, but you're a sight for sore eyes,' he said. 'Quite the woman
about town now?'

Orla reddened. 'And yourself?'

'Tired.'

Orla looked Sean up and down, each time raising her gaze
another inch as though Sean was turning giant before her.

'Well?' Sean laughed. 'Do I pass inspection? Am I still Sean
Joseph Byrne, brother of Orla?'

A frown flickered across Orla's face but then she grinned.

'Let's go home,' she said.

*

Sean's suitcase hit at knees and hands as they pushed a path forwards
through the forest of dark-coated people. He thought of the papers
he'd slipped inside the case's lining.

'Mammy can't wait to see you,' Orla said.

'Likewise,' said Sean.

Orla paused. 'Likewise?'

'Yes.'

'That's a queer expression.'

'Sounds ordinary enough to me. I feel the same. Likewise.'

'Is it English?'

A drop of rain trickled under Sean's collar. 'Don't we speak English?'

Orla stared again. 'You look different too. Changed.'

Sean's back stiffened as he kept walking. Only five minutes had passed, and already they were having this conversation. Every word he said now would be turned over, examined, like a stone that might or might not be fit for skimming.

'Swankier,' Orla went on.

'Swankier?' he said.

Sean looked down at his creased shirt and trousers, clothes that hadn't seen a bar of soap for too many days now. It would have been Mam who'd first sown these questions in Orla's head. 'Will he be changed? Will he feel he's too good for us now?' She would have made an evensong of her doubts every night since he'd left; and his little sister, who held the family's voices inside her, repeated her words now. It had sometimes worried Sean – Orla's mimicry – as though she didn't possess even the beginnings of her own voice. And yet here he was himself, come to repeat other men's reasons.

'Listen,' he said as Orla caught up with him. 'I've not gone up in the world. Shovelling cement and laying bricks, even if they have the King's crown on them – it doesn't open a better class of doors to you. They just pay more over there. Sure isn't that why I went?'

Orla's ears turned into little beetroots and Sean knew she heard the lie. Da's death had given him permission to leave, it was true. The need for money had been their emergency, but it had never been Sean's reason for leaving.

Orla nudged him. 'We're just glad you're home, so. Everyone's glad. All the mothers up and down our street will be hanging on their front doors, waiting to see you.'

Sean smiled, even as he detected the mockery, or maybe the prickle of envy, in his sister's voice. He let himself imagine it for a moment: the mothers standing on their doorsteps, faces powdered, their arms unfolding in one synchronised wave as they heard his footsteps. 'Welcome home, son,' they might croon. 'Sean Byrne – blue-eyed and silver-tongued and faithful, just like his old Da.' Just like his Da, until the TB had grabbed hold of him; just like Da until the stubborn pride had risen in him and he'd refused to enter the sanatorium. 'I'm not leaving my home,' he'd said. 'No doctors or wild horses or women or even my son can make me. I'll stay here till they carry me out.' And he had stayed, until Sean had found him in his armchair that morning. And he could see the door open again now, amongst this crowd. The door swung, and there was Da's arm hanging limp against the chair, his knuckles grazing the floor, the forefinger curled just above the thumb as though he wanted a pen. And if Da could write to him now from any afterlife, Sean knew what he'd say. *Stay home. Take my chair. I left it for you.*

And there was Sean's reason for leaving the first time; and his reason for leaving again.

*

A pulley of wires sparked blues and golds as they reached the tram stop. Sean wished one spark would land in his opening mouth and strike him dumb so he might write his decision in a letter and not have to speak it aloud to Mam and Orla.

Another wire sparked red and he saw the muscles flex in Orla's shoulder as she leaned back against the lamppost. It surprised him, this glimpsed strength, like the strapping arms a swan bared when she raised her wings. And he remembered that restless night back in England, when he'd decided to sign up – and how he'd dreamt of her. His little sister was swimming the breadth of the Irish Sea beneath a half moon. The next moment there she was, at the door of his Nissen hut, drenched and smiling. 'It's a bleeding mermaid,' one of the other men said. Orla had let out a shivery laugh. 'A woman,' she'd said and grabbed a spade as Sean opened his eyes to the morning.

'Orla?' Sean tapped her now on the shoulder.

'Yes?'

'I'm going to sign up. Do my bit.'

She didn't blink. 'I know.'

'You know?'

Her shoulders rose. 'Sure I can read a face, Sean. And letters that spare no words for home.'

He reddened.

'Did I never occur to you?' she asked.

'What?'

Orla pointed towards the harbour. 'Did you never think I'd want my turn? My chance over there? A nurse? A lifeguard? Someone? Somewhere else?'

Sean said nothing. Orla turned away.

'Just don't tell Mammy. Not tonight. Pretend you're staying. Pretend her dearest son's back where he belongs.' Her voice fell. 'Sit in Da's chair.'

She nodded towards that stone-cold body.

'Pretend you've not left that place for me.'

Alan Gillespie
THE ARCADE

The old man waited. Stood holding an umbrella next to the Argyll Arcade's side entrance. He wore a good navy suit and waistcoat, a white shirt with the top button open. The crowds on Buchanan Street moved quickly through the rain although it was not as heavy as forecast.

The woman appeared beside him and made him jump. Well, she said, here I am. She had a thick, silver fringe and big brown eyes. Short eyelashes and warm-looking cheeks. She looked older but better than in the photographs he'd seen online. A bright orange scarf wrapped around and across her shoulders.

Gaynor, the man smiled. Thank you for coming. I'm Bill.

I know, she said. I recognise you. Do I look all right, then?

He stepped back and made a theatre of appraising her outfit and said that she looked perfect. He touched her shoulder, folded up his umbrella and shook off the rainwater. Are you ready? he asked.

You haven't even told me where we're going.

Just in here.

He put his hand out as a guide and they stepped into the Arcade, lined on both sides with jewellery shops. A few other couples stood side by side looking at diamonds and antique watches. It was quiet. The security guard wore a top hat that was a little too large. He nodded, his moustache drooping, blazer frayed at the cuffs. Afternoon, he said to them. Bill replied with a wink.

The woman raised her eyebrows. What are we doing here?

Browsing. I think you'll like it.

They stopped first outside the window of Laings. The upper display was all watches, and below that, diamond rings. The pink copper of rose gold, the snowy flash of platinum.

Which ring would you choose?

She frowned at him.

If you had to? he asked.

She placed both palms flat against the cold window's surface. I don't like any of them.

None?

Nope.

He pointed at an expensive range near the back of the display. Those ones are nice, he said. The jewellery nestled in pale green cushions. One of the salesgirls who worked in the shop came through the door and smiled at them. Her makeup was pristine and she wore black tights with black heeled shoes.

Are you looking for anything specific?

The woman was about to say no, but Bill interrupted. We're looking for an engagement ring, he said. For my beautiful fiancée.

The salesgirl smiled widely. Congratulations! Why don't we step inside. We have lots of rings to choose from. She rubbed Gaynor's arm and held the door open for them.

Well, asked Bill. Gaynor was staring at him, her fingers stretched out in front of her.

What are you doing, she whispered. No, no.

Trust me.

She looked back towards the security guard and the drizzle of Buchanan Street beyond the Arcade's exit.

Stay just for a minute, he said. It'll be okay.

She walked past him and into the shop, smiling at the girl, and Bill came in behind her.

The old man and his date sat side by side on a purple couch. The salesgirl put a bottle of sparkling water with two glasses on the table in front of them. The room had soft lighting and textured wallpaper. A thick carpet. So, she said. Do you know what you're looking for?

We're open minded, said the man. Aren't we, darling?

Wonderful. We have lots of different options. Do you have a budget in mind?

Gaynor looked at Bill. She tightened her scarf around her.

I'm thinking, he said, we can go to about ten thousand.

Fantastic, said the girl. We've got some really special pieces in that price range. But first let me get you two some champagne, to celebrate.

She went downstairs and left Bill and Gaynor sitting on the couch.

Ten thousand?

Sure, he said. You're worth it.

The salesgirl returned with two flutes and a bottle of champagne. She tore at the foil and twisted the cork from the bottle. For the next twenty minutes, they talked about diamonds, their clarity, their unlikeliness. About settings and precious metals. The salesgirl asked the man how he had proposed.

Oh, there's a story there, said the woman. Isn't there, honey?

Bill pushed the wispy hair back on his head and sipped his champagne. We were in Paris, he said, over Easter. The girl filled both their drinks again as he spoke. I'd bought a padlock from Timpson's and had it engraved on one side with both our names, inside a wee love-heart. We took it to the bridge over the river with all the love locks – I knew they were taking the padlocks down but we wanted to anyway. So we went. All the railings are covered in them. From all over the world. It was sunny – remember, darling? – and the padlocks were glittering. Like diamonds. Like stars. He took Gaynor's hand in his. And you chose a wee blank patch on the fence. I had the padlock in my pocket, and I gave it to you. Turn it over, I said. On the other side I'd had the engraver put four more words. Will you marry me?, it said. And I got down onto this old man's knee, and you said yes, and I said well, if you want a kiss you'll need to help me back to my feet. And that was that.

Gaynor looked to the ceiling and shook her head.

The salesgirl was beaming. That's some story, she said.

It's one of my best, he said.

They stayed in Laings for an hour, drinking champagne, giggling on the couch, and looking at rings. Gaynor slipped emeralds and big diamonds and deep blue sapphires over the joints of her old finger. Finally she stood up. Thank you for all your help, she said to the salesgirl. We'll be back. So many nice rings, I need to mull it over. She turned to Bill. Let's go. I don't think we should rush it, honey.

The salesgirl gave the man a business card. Ask for me when you come back in, she said. And congratulations again.

The couple left Laings arm in arm. A little drunk.

Do you date many men? he wanted to know.

Gaynor untangled Bill's arm from hers. Some. Not many.

You're very good at it. I feel comfortable around you.

Thank you, Bill. I feel at ease with you too. How about you, are you taking lots of women out?

Only you so far.

So far?

Bill paused and Gaynor started to laugh. When he saw she wasn't upset, he laughed too.

They stopped outside Ernest Jones. What do you fancy trying on this time, he asked.

Earrings, she said.

Budget?

Twenty grand.

Another good-looking salesgirl with thick, immaculate eyebrows took them inside.

We're celebrating our silver wedding anniversary, explained Bill. And my wife wants a pair of earrings.

Wonderful, said the girl. Do you know what style you want?

I like all of them, said the woman.

Do you have an idea of how much you'd like to spend? Roughly?

Twenty thousand pounds, said the woman. Roughly.

And the man threw his head back and laughed.

They split another bottle of fizz while the girl brought the earrings. Sitting opposite one another at a low table. Bill leaned forward, cradling his chin in his hands. Gaynor had taken off her scarf and had her silver hair swept back from her face. He could see the wrinkles framing her eyes. She held up the earrings to her lobes, rotating her head, making the pendants dangle and move. An illuminated mirror picked up the sparkle from the jewellery, the colours in her eyes, the texture of her skin.

The old man watched and sipped slowly from his glass. Those are beautiful, he might say. Gorgeous, he called another pair.

When the bottle was finished Gaynor looked at him. Well, she said, what do you think? Shall we take these ones? She held a pair of pearl-drop earrings.

You like those ones, darling?

No, honey. I love these ones.

He scratched his nose. We'll need to have a think about it. We'll come back in.

Of course, the salesgirl smiled. No rush. I'll be here all afternoon.

When they left the shop, the rain outside had grown heavier. The polished Arcade floor was wet from people dragging their umbrellas through.

How did your wife die? she asked. The fingertips of the rain tapped on the Arcade's glass roof.

It was lots of things, in the end, said Bill. He cleared his throat, fist to his chest.

You don't want to talk about it.

I can talk about it. She was sick for a long time. I looked after her. Then she needed more help, so she went into a care home. She got much better, then she got much worse. By the end she had lots of problems. Every day there was something new, some part of her body shutting down.

You must have been a great comfort to her.

I wish she had died in her own home. Why do you ask?

I wanted to know you more.

Are you doing okay? he smiled.

I'm great.

Having a good time?

I am.

Shall we try another one?

She lifted her head, cheeks pink from the drink. Over here, she said, and tugged him across to Chisholm Hunter at the other side of the Arcade. The window had a lot of men's watches, silver links and black leather. There were pocket-watches made of gold and ceremonial tie pins. Come on, she said, and they went straight into the shop.

They sat on high stools at a polished countertop. A skinny boy wearing a tight white shirt came to see to them. Gaynor accepted some sparkling water and then told the boy that they were here to try on some watches for her husband.

Very good, said the boy. He poured them a glass of prosecco but did not leave the bottle.

Bill took off his coat and rolled his right sleeve up to the elbow, turning the cuff over twice. His skin was pale but the arm was thick, with veins mapped out across his wrist and the back of his hand. There was still muscle. Gaynor touched him there and felt the warmth coming through the thin old skin.

How long were you married for? he whispered.

Five years.

That doesn't seem like long enough.

It was long enough for us to know we were wasting our time, living like that. Never happy, never enough. We used to have these terrible fights. Tearing into each other. Neither of us could remember how they'd started or what the problem was. Then we worked it out that the problem was just us.

And you never thought about marrying again.

I thought about it. Never met anyone else who did though.

You're still young enough. There's still time for that again.

So are you. So there is.

The boy came from through the back with a selection of watches for Bill to try on. The link chains felt heavy on his arm but Gaynor thought they suited him.

Too much like a bracelet, he said. I've always preferred a leather strap. He picked at a spot of dry skin on his arm.

It's good to try something new, honey.

He looked at the boy. Such a wise woman, he said.

Is there a special occasion, asked the boy, hands in his pockets.

My husband, said Gaynor, he's finally retiring.

Good for you, said the boy. What line of work were you in?

Piracy, she said. First it was tape cassettes. He punted them around all the pubs. Then video tapes. You won't remember those. Then came the CDs, and the DVDs. PlayStation games. Blu-ray. He was the best pirate in Scotland.

Bill laughed quietly at this.

But you can't pirate an iPhone, can you? she said.

No, darling, agreed Bill. You cannot.

The boy was stuck. Have you known each other for long? he asked.

We met at school, said Gaynor. Didn't we, honey. Remember we used to sit next to each other in art class. You used to always flick your paintbrush at me. I'd be covered in little specks of pink and black and white, all the way up my wrist and arm, all over my shirt.

Did I? I don't remember that, said Bill. We used to hold hands under the desk. Didn't we, darling?

Gaynor smiled. Sometimes you would reach for my legs and feel me up, she said. The teacher caught you doing it and told your mother.

Bill turned to the boy. She's lying, obviously. I married a complete fantasist.

Gaynor leaned across to Bill and touched the tip of her nose against his. I think we should leave this young man to his afternoon.

I do, too.

Let me give you my card, said the boy. In case you want to come back in and have another look.

I won't, said Bill. No offence, son. I'm just not bothered about keeping track of time anymore.

They left the shop, hand in hand. Walked slowly past Fraser Hart and Bernstones. Going slower, admiring the window displays. Until they got to the old security guard at the other end of the Arcade. Gaynor dropped Bill's hand from hers.

Thank you, Bill. This was fun.

It's been a long time since I spent such a good afternoon with such a good woman.

My bus is this way. She was stepping slowly backwards out of the Arcade.

We could go into Sloans for one more?

I'm getting a headache. All that champagne.

Well, okay. Thank you for meeting me today.

Thank you for asking me.

I thoroughly enjoyed myself.

I did too. I should go. I'm worried I might miss my bus.

Would you like to do this again? Not this, not the same thing, but something different. With me.

I don't know. I'm not used to this.

But neither am I.

I have your phone number.

You do.

I'll have to think about it.

So you might call. Or you might not. That's okay, Gaynor. Either way.

If I don't call, she said, please don't be upset.

I can't promise that.

If I don't call, she said, it doesn't mean I didn't have a nice time. This was a good date. I'll tell people about it. I think this will make a nice story one day.

She wrapped her scarf tightly around her neck and stepped out of the Arcade onto Argyll Street. She paused until there was a gap in the shoppers and then turned into the crowd, joining them and their flow.

The noise of a drumming band bounced around the street. Bill fastened each button on his coat and the cold wind wandered past him into the Arcade, where all the jewellery still sparkled even though the weather was turning.

Jennifer Harvey
SOMETHING RED AND SMALL AND CRUMPLED

One of those early days of Spring. Sunshine bright, but with a chill in the air, enough to keep coats buttoned up, but not enough to keep people indoors; the sun warming Amsterdam back to life again after another damp, grey winter. The café terraces are busy, people everywhere, drinking and chatting, laughing and relaxing. There are birds too, chirruping in the still-bare branches. They know that winter is coming to an end, and that is reason enough to sing.

The café where they sit, makes the best espresso in town, so strong it gives you goosebumps. It's why she'd insisted on meeting there and not at that other, cheaper place on the Prinsengracht Ella prefers. Such are the insignificant details on which decisions turn. Fateful, only when you look back.

Four euros fifty for a coffee is ridiculous, of course it is. But as she sips the espresso and feels the warmth of the sun on her face, she stops feeling guilty for bringing Ella here. And she looks over at Ella to check she is okay with it all, and sees her eyes are closed, her face is turned towards the sun. She is quiet and smiling. Good.

'I'm glad we came here,' she says.

And Ella nods, open her eyes and mutters, 'uh-huh,' while stirring a spoon of sugar into her coffee cup.

Later, she will think there should be a word to describe when a moment of happiness, such as this, turns from light to shade. Something German and unpronounceable. Untranslatable too, because who really wants to understand such a thing?

But for now, it is the balloon which catches her eye, some helium confection, yellow and bright, floating on a string. She watches it and tunes out Ella's voice. She's talking again about all that business with Frans, a story she's heard a thousand times already, and today she does not feel like listening. But Ella drones on, the odd snippet filtering through despite her best efforts to push it away: '... it's the lack of imagination ... it's not that I don't want to talk to him, it's more, well ... what about? ... Gina thought perhaps a holiday, just the two of us together, but I don't know. What do you think? I mean, maybe ...'

Good God, she thinks. Why can't you simply enjoy the moment? Just let the morning fall away, all loose and relaxed and free from indignation. Why do you have to talk at all?

Ella hasn't noticed the balloon. She hasn't heard the birds chirrup or the teaspoons chink against the coffee cups. She hasn't shivered with that little jolt of pleasure good coffee always brings.

And she thinks: maybe it's not Frans who's lacking in imagination? and keeps watching the balloon as it bobs above the line of cars parked along the pavement. She smiles when she recognises it: Pikachu, and finds herself amused by the contrast of the cartoon figure against the elegant gables of the canal-side houses. Twice she catches sight of the boy, a brief glimpse of blond hair and a red t-shirt. He is skipping along, and he is happy, just as she is.

And then he runs, this happy boy with the balloon, and she watches and thinks, 'Well, why not? I would too if I were him. If I were a boy with a Pikachu balloon, bobbing down the street on a bright Spring day I would run and run and run.'

Though later, the mother – at least she assumes it is the mother – will say: 'He just ran. I don't know why. He just ran. Straight into the street.'

And it was true, he did. He ran out between the cars and on to the road. She saw him – a flash of yellow and red. She heard him too – the thud he made. She blinked and saw the balloon float up and away and it took her a moment to understand what she had witnessed. The car stopped on the street, someone screaming, wailing. The balloon rising and rising. And there on the ground, something red and small and crumpled.

But in that instant, as she registers the thud and what it means, all she can say is, 'Oh!' as she stands up, knocks the table, and tips over her coffee. The contents spill and spatter Ella's new, white skirt. A stain that will never wash out.

'Damn it, Louise,' she hears Ella yell. 'My new skirt.'

But she is running now too. Running to the road, running to the boy. Not knowing what she will do when she reaches him. Just running.

If Ella had understood why she ran, she would have stopped her. Made sure she didn't reach him. Made sure she didn't kneel down beside him, and smooth away the hair from his face, and say to him, 'Everything will be okay, everything will be okay,' while the mother wailed, and someone shouted to, 'Call an ambulance,' and the birds, those damn birds, kept right on chirruping.

She would not have worried about the coffee stain on her new skirt. She would not have cursed and fussed and thought, 'Why is she always so careless with people?' Those insignificant details again, on which each moment turns.

No, she would have held her back, looked her in the eye, and told her there was nothing she could do. She would have saved Louise from the memory which will come to haunt her. The boy's blue eyes, bright as ice in the sun, then darkening as the pupils dilated.

But it is too late. There is no going back now. It is done. The coffee spilled. The balloon rising. The boy crumpled.

So there is no stopping it – the flow of memory, year after year. Spring comes around, and Louise remembers what she saw: 'He was there, and then he was gone,' while Ella remembers the coffee stain as it spread across the white of her skirt and thinks: 'I could have saved her from this torment. If it wasn't for a spilled coffee cup, I could have saved her from this.'

But in that moment, there is only chaos and noise and confusion. Ella stares at her skirt, Louise runs, a mother wails, and Pikachu, Pikachu floats above the rooftops and across the city, and people, blocks away, look up and point and smile and say, 'Hey, look! Pikachu!' While Ella's coffee, in its Delft blue cup, grows cold.

Lauren Ivers
JOHN

In my father's house
are many rooms.
He says that God
lives in every one.

Lingering in grey dust
of the fake coal
fireplace. Vanishing
up the chimney
when it's hot.

In damp darkness
of the pulled shower
curtain, he waits
between the razor
and the soap.

He hides in the kitchen
junk drawer,
among rubber bands
and batteries.

God lives at my dad's house.
I visit him there sometimes.

Russell Jones
BEORN

I've been told the story of the sky:
dandelion seeds and dragon wings,
sifted dust and the flare of suns.

I'll pull you over the heather hills,
kick gravestones, ignore the whispers
of wind through trees.

At the peak is a great old bear,
grey and slow. We can ask
about hibernation, but she will reply:

When you sleep, do you worry
you'll never wake? Do you cry
at the blossoming city

or weep when the woods shrink?
She will sit and think (she is very wise),
brew tea, hold us in her pillow-soft arms,

her heart thudding like heavy rain,
until our hearts adopt her rhythm
just as we've always wanted.

David Ross Linklater
HOUSE BY THE DIVINE

The sea is a silver crop.
    Old chicken coop the ribs of a cherry bush.
Ploughs send their iron hands into the earth,
    opening fields, unburdening them.

It's near perfect to lean on the garden
    wall where there is no question.
Dirt lungs, the voices of gone men
    bundled in corners of pig sheds.

It has been raised from pulpits that heaven
    is somewhere to gain. Home, others call it.
In the bark of oak we carve our memory,
    initial the salt-laced wind.

Days of chimney stacks, rain dances.
    Oh country moon, your white horse, your red door
beckon, chimes in your greenhouse call.
    Holy kindling, revolutions of garden shears.

Organs of the land invested.
    The soil is turned, beaks cover in dirt
searching for pink blessings that curl
    and give life for another season.

Vines have delivered their pale vision.
    There will be more photographs, sore hands, bones,
eyes going a bit, but fate is just a word.
    This body is a machine, a powerful born-to-haul thing.

The further you get the neater your woodpile.
    Old man, this wheelbarrow is good for racing yet.
Another log on the fire, then, get her stoked.
    Only the hills know where we go from here.

Aoife Lyall
SOUNDS OF THAT DAY

(after Norman MacCaig)

When a silence came,
it was your heart not beating.
When the door hushed, it was
the shuffle of a midwife leaving
us alone in our private grief. A muffled clanging
ten yards down the corridor was the news breaking and
unbreaking in the filing cabinet.
When the black biro rolled, it was me
falling and falling into myself.

When the door
clicked shut behind us, it was the end
of all the silences there were.

They left us
in the busiest corridor in the hospital.

I thought I was hurt in my body only
not knowing that
when your body sleeps
your mind feels all those kicks
in your round stomach before you wake
and the whole world goes numb.

Crìsdean MacIlleBhàin
MO SHEARMON (II)

Mo shearmon mar latha tiamhaidh fadalach ann an Glaschu
agus na frasan a' tuiteam is a' tuiteam,
bhiodh dùil agad sin a bhith inntinneach no
caochlaideach
ach tha marbhantachd san taisbeanadh
a chuireadh neach sam bith
ri speuran nas coibhneil' a shireadh,
saoghal nach eil liath is glas a-mhàin
mar a thachras leis an fhear seo,
saoghal far am biodh na dathan gu lèir
a' nochdadh 'nan làn-iomadachd –
shaoileadh tu na cuantan a bhith air am falmhachadh
leis an uiread a dh'uisge a tha air dòrtadh sìos
gun eadar-dhàil no lughdachadh ach
a chlisge creididh tu gun do sguir e,
am bualadh trom mar dhrumaireachd air na duilleagan
a thug an naidheachd an samhradh a bhith air tighinn
gu Glaschu aig a' cheann thall –
mun cuairt ort tha 'n aimsir a' fàs
nas ciùine, tostaiche, seallaidh tu
a-mach bhon uinneig, 's tu deiseal ri bòideachadh
gun tàinig stad air tuil nan tuil a bh' ann –
ach chì thu gu bheil thu ceàrr,
ma nì thu sgrùdadh nas gèire
mothaichear do sheòrsa ceò san adhar
nach eil 'na cheò fìor,
tha driùchd mhaoth shèimh a' tighinn a-nuas fhathast,
cha do sguir an t-uisge idir!
Mo shearmon a bhios uaireannan 'na phlangaid
luchdail sprèideach 's iomadh preas 'na meadhan
a chòmhdaicheas gu fàilteachail na thig fo dìon

coltach ris a' phlangaid a chunnaic bana-charaid agam
a rugadh ann an Naples agus a bha ag obair
ann a-sin a' tadhal air na daoine bochd
gus gach cobhair is taic a ghabhadh
a thairgse 's a sholarachadh dhaibh
ach b' e an cùram sònraichte aice
feuchainn am b' urrainn do na pàistean uile
nochdadh anns an sgoil choitchinn
far am b' fheudar do gach neach a dhol
nuair a ruigeadh e 'n aois fhreagarrach –
thuirt ise rium nach fhaca i a-chaoidh
taigh cho bochd, daibhir, ainniseach
dh'fhaodadh a ràdh nach robh àirneis eile ann
seach a' phlangaid ana-mhòr, àireamh gun fhios
de chloinn bhig gan cruinneachadh foipe
còmhla ri am màthair, gun lorg ann
air athair no athraichean, agus na luchan
a' tighinn 's a' teicheadh 's a' ruith
measg filltean na plangaid gun a' chlann
a bhith toirt an aire as lugha
do ghàrradh nam beathaichean a bh' ann a-sin –
bhiodh am màthair a' cosnadh na dh'fhòghnadh
gu biadh is deoch a cheannach dhaibh uile
's i leughadh naidheachdan an ama ri teachd
bho chairtean àrsaidh ioma-dhathte,
sgeadaichte le dreachan samhlachail
a bha gan glèidheadh cuideachd fon phlangaid,
dh'fhaighnich i dhen bhana-charaid agam
nach bu mhiann leatha fios a bhith aice
dè bha dol a thachairt sna mìosan ri tighinn
cha robh i ag iarraidh airgid,
bha sin a-mhàin 'na dhearbhadh air dè

cho toilichte 's a bha i aoigh a bhith aca san taigh –
thuirt mo bhana-charaid nach ann a thaobh sin
a thàinig ise, agus gun dàil
dh'fhaighnich a' mhàthair nach biodh i 'g iarraidh
cofaidh dubh làidir a ghabhail còmhla,
bha cofaidh anabarrach blasta aice
ach bha mo bhana-charaid fo eagal 's i smaoineachadh
ciod e an seòrsa mheanbh-bhiastagan
a dh'fhaodadh a bhith fuireachd ann an inneal-chofaidh
ann an taigheadas mar sin,
dh'innis i cuideachd dhomh
gu robh e mìorbhaileach an dòigh chùirteil
ghaolach air an robh a' mhathair a' bruidhinn
ris an t-sìol gu lèir a bh' aice
agus an coibhneas is an t-urram
leis an sealladh a clann oirre,
's iad deiseal ri gach facal a thuirt i
a leantainn, gach òrdugh a choilionadh –
cha b' ionnan sin ri latha eile
mar a chualas leatha 'n dèidh làimhe
nuair a thàinig màthair dhan togalach
san robh an oifig aic' le daga
falaichte 'na baga-làimhe
agus rùn aice a bhith losgadh
air mo bhana-charaid on a bha i creidsinn
gu robh 'n aon phàiste a bh' aice
a' dol a bhith ga thoirt air falbh
's nach dèanadh i fhaicinn
uair eile gu ceann a beatha
Mo shearmon a tha cho farsaing fàilteachail
  's gum bi àit' ann, mar fon phlangaid
  sprèidich sin an Naples (chan eil mi

airson an càineadh idir, chan eil mi 'g ràdh
gur luchan bearraideach sgreamhail,
doirbh ri glacadh a th' annta)
airson nan sgrùdair agam – nach sgìtheil
mì-thaingeil an dreuchd a th' aca! 's iad
a' sìor-rannsachadh gach easbhaidh is croin
ann an dàn no ann an leabhar
is fhios againn uile gu bheil iad a' tuigsinn
na bha ann an inntinn an ùghdair, no na bha e
'g amas air nuair a thoisich e air sgrìobhadh
fada nas fheàrr na 'n t-ùghdar bochd fhèin
agus gum biodh iad air an oidhirp gu lèir
a choilionadh 's a thoirt gu buil air dòigh
mòran na bu mhaisiche, rìomhaiche, abalt'
ach ùine gu leòr a bhith aca
bhon a tha iad an còmhnaidh cho trang
a' luachadh 's a' toirt binn
air saothraichean dhaoine eile –
saoilidh mi gum bi e 'na iongantas
anabarrach tlachdmhor dhaibh
faighinn a-mach gu bheil iad a' nochdadh
mar-thà ann an obair nach d' fhuair iad
cothrom air a leughadh gus a-seo, an àit'
a bhith sgrìobhadh earr-ràdh bhig thruaghanta
a thèid a chlò-bhualadh ann am pàipear-naidheachd
no ann an iris air choreigin –
Eachann, mar eisempleir,
a tha air cantainn rium a-cheana
(bidh na beachdan a th' aig na sgrùdairean agam
air an copaigeadh an seo sa Bheurla
bhon as àbhaist leotha an cur an cèill
sa chànan sin a-mhàin, neo-ar-thaing

gur ann ri teacsa sgrìobhta anns a' Ghàidhlig
a bhios iad a' dèiligeadh) (ris an fhìrinn innse,
cha bhi mar as trice aon chànan
seach a' Bheurla aca, chan fhaic iad
cnap-starra no cuibhreachadh ann a-sin)
bha cuid mhòr dhe sgrùdairean uamhasach taingeil
gun do theab Somhairle Beurla a chur
air gach uile dàn a rinn e
agus iomadh sgoilear is fear-teòma
nach tuigear leis dad sa Ghàidhlig
a' glaodhaich gu h-àrd is buaireanta
am beachd a th' aig' air a bhàrdachd,
's iad a' smaoineachadh, cò aig a bheil fhios?
gum b' urrainn don bhàrd a' chuid a bu mhotha
dhe spàirn a sheachnadh nan robh e
air leum a dhèanamh air adhart, is gach aon
spreigeadh a thàinig air bhon Cheòlraidh
a chur sìos sa Bheurla anns a' chiad àite –
nach biodh sin fada na bu reusanta? –
tha iomadh bàrd nas òig' ann a chreideas
gur ann air an guailnean fhèin a thuit
mantal Shomhairle 's e tuiteam bho na speuran – ·
cho luath is a bhios dàn Gàidhlig crìochnaicht' aca
bidh cabhag orra a thionndadh chun na Beurla
gun a bhith cinnteach ciod am fear
dhe na dhà a b' fheàrr a shoirbhich leotha –
chan eil teagamh ann, their Eachann uair eile
You've got such an astonishingly
puerile sense of humour –
agus am proifeasar iomraiteach, cliùiteach
a thuirt air an rèidio, ann am prògram
mu dheidhinn bàrdachd Dheòrsa Mhic Iain Dheòrsa

Nobody can write poetry
in a language he didn't dream in as a child
a' tilgeil mar sin dhan sgùileach
a h-uile dàin a sgrìobh Deòrsa sa Ghàidhlig
ged nach b' urrainn dha aon loidhne dhiubh
a leughadh air fad a bheatha,
bidh e 'g aithris an aon bheachd 'nam chàs,
tha mi cinnteach – chan eil feum aig an fheadhainn sin
air dearbhadh no rannsachadh sam bith,
is am barail a' mairsinn stèidhichte
cunbhalach às an eugmhais –
agus Ise, nach robh cho mhathasach
sa bhreithneachadh a thug I air dàintean Dheòrsa
ged a b' urrainn Dhi an leughadh sa Ghàidhlig,
their I, math dh'fhaodte, mar a thubhairt
mu rudeigin eil' a thug mise fo h-aire
I just don't see the point of doing that –
ach Teàrlach Mòr, a bha dripeil, torrach
'g ath-sgrìobhadh bàrdachd Mhic Mhaighstir Alastair
no Dhonnchaidh Bhàin gun eòlas aige
ach air beagan fhaclan Gàidhlig, mar a dh'aidich e
gun nàire – nach bu chòir fosgarrachd
cho ionmholta onarach a bhith molta
gun aon sgrubal? – dè tha e dol a ràdh?
an dèan e tionndadh Beurla air an dàn seo cuideachd
gun seantans no briathar dheth thuigsinn,
gun dragh sam bith thaobh brìgh no seagh,
's e cur ris, mar a rinn e a-cheana
le obraichean ùghdaran mòran nas cudromaiche
earrannan nuadha nach do sgrìobh mi riamh
's nach sgrìobhar leams' a-chaoidh?

Mo shearmon mar mo sheanmhair nuair a bha i uamhasach
   aosta
is a thigeadh i air aoigheachd
ann an taigh mo phàrantan
agus bhiodh i a' cadal air a' chùiste mhòir
anns an t-seòmar-chòmhnaidh
agus dhiùltadh i buileach an doras a dhùnadh
bhon a bha i car mì-fhoisneach anns gach àite
a dh'fhairich i a bhith teann is dinnte
is a bharrachd air sin bha eagal oirre
daonnan ro na taibhsean, chan fhacas taibhse riamh
anns an taigh le neach sam bith
ach is dòcha gun do chreid i
gum b' urrainn dha na taibhsean aice fhèin
a leantainn anns gach ceàrn san robh i dol
is mar sin, 's an doras fosgailte,
chualas gu soilleir àrd an t-srannail
oillteil, mhaoimeach a dhèanadh i –
smaoinicheadh tu gun do thòisich iad
a' cladhach suas uachdar na sràide
dìreach fa chomhair an togalaich
leis na h-innleachdan anabarrach mòr
a dh'ùisnicheas iad an-diugh,
air neo gu robh plèanaichean ar nàmhaid
air tighinn gun rabhadh a bhomaigeadh a' bhaile –
bha sinn uile fo àmhghar,
na h-inbhich is a' chlann gun dòchas
air mionaid cadail fhaighinn fad na h-oidhche,
ach an uair sin thòisicheadh cuideigin a' gàireachdaich
agus beag air bheag cha b' urrainn da h-uile duine
ach gàir' a dhèanamh, is thuiteadh gach aon 'na chadal

gun fhiost' air mar a bha sin a' tachairt
agus sa mhadainn, a' gabhail ar bracaist,
bha e gu leòr fear dhinn an sealladh
ann an sùilean fir eile a ghlacadh
is bhiodh an gàireachdaich a' tilleadh
agus dh'fheòraicheadh a' chailleach
gu dè an spòrs a bh' againn uile
's e ga cheiltinn bhuaipe
ach cha do dh'innis sinn idir
agus, an dèidh dhi dol dhachaigh,
sna leapannan, b' e an spòrs cò dhèanadh
an atharrais a b' fheàrr air an torranach
uamhasach a thigeadh a-mach
bhon t-sròin bhig aig granaidh 's i 'na cadal
Mo shearmon 's e a' teannachadh gu crìch
mar an cadal a' buannachd ort beag is beag
fairichidh tu e ann am badan dhe do bhodhaig
no 's dòcha gur e bloighean dhe mhosgalachd
dha bheil thu mothachadh, bho nach urrainn
do dhuine a bhith fiosrach mu theàrnadh a' chadail
seòrsa dìochuimhneachaidh a th' ann
faodaidh e bhith mar làn-mara a' sìor buannachd
air an tràigh, ga ceannsachadh gu fiatach,
teachd is tilleadh nan tonn cho coltach ris
an iomlaid shìorraidh bhios aig t' analachadh –
caillear leat gluasad tuinn uair 's a-rithist
ann am mòmaid thig an t-iongnadh ort
's cho beag de ghaineimh a' mairsinn fhathast
theab a' mhuir an tràigh gu lèir a bhuannachd
tha t' fhiosrachadh air gach ball a thrèigsinn
le neart na cadalachd is i do-bhacadh
do smuain air fògradh, chan eil dòigh air ràdh

ciod e an tèarmann a chuireas fàilt' air
tha e math dh'fhaodt' 'na shiubhlaiche air bàta
fhathast nach deach dìreach à sealladh
'na shanas lag an àiteigin san fhàire
'na smal gun dreach dheimhinnt' aig bun nan speur
's tus' thu fhèin mar choinneal ga sèideadh às.

Christopher Whyte
THE WAY I TALK (II)

The way I talk, like an endless melancholy Glasgow day
    the rain showers falling and falling
    you would think it could be interesting or varied
    but the spectacle has something deathly about it
    that would set anybody
    looking for gentler climes,
    for a world that's not as grey and dreary
    as this one is, a world
    where the whole gamut of colours
    would be displayed –
    the very oceans must have dried out
    with the quantity of water that pours down
    no hint of lessening or intermission –
    all a sudden you imagine it's stopped,
    that heavy percussion like drums on the leaves
    bringing news that summer has arrived,
    as you look around the weather
    seems calmer and quieter, you glance
    out of the window, ready to swear
    that the downpour has come to an end –
    but you see that you're wrong,
    if you look more closely
    you notice a sort of mistiness in the air
    which is not real mist, but a mild
    and gentle dampness still descending,
    it hasn't stopped raining at all!
The way I talk, sometimes like a capacious
    spreading blanket with lots of folds
    whose cover welcomes all those needing protection
    like the blanket a woman friend of mine
    born in Naples saw, she worked

visiting poor people to offer them
whatever support and help was available
but her particular responsibility
was trying to make sure all the children
turned up each day at school
where they were obliged to go
after reaching the appropriate age –
she told me she had never seen
such a poor, destitute, deprived home
practically the only furnishing they had
was the huge blanket, numerous children
huddling underneath it
together with their mother, no sign
of a father or fathers, and mice
running backwards and forwards between
the folds of the blanket, without the children
paying the slightest bit of attention
to that veritable zoo surrounding them –
their mother earned enough money
to buy food and drink for everyone there
reading off the future from brilliantly coloured
ancient cards decorated with images
which were also kept under the blanket –
she asked my friend if she would like to know
what was going to happen in the months ahead,
she didn't want any payment, it was merely
in order to show how delighted it made her
having a guest there in their home,
my friend said that wasn't
what she had come for, and immediately
the mother asked if she wouldn't enjoy

drinking some strong black coffee together,
the coffee she had was excellently flavoured
but my friend was wondering fearfully
what sort of tiny beasties might make their home
in the coffee pot in a household of that sort,
she also told me how marvellously polite
and loving the way the mother
addressed all of her offspring was,
not to mention the affection and respect
in the children's eyes when they looked
at her, ready to follow her instructions,
to carry out every order she gave –
that was very different from the day
she learned after it happened that a mother
had come to the building where she had her office
carrying a pistol hidden in her handbag
planning to fire it at my friend because
she was convinced the only child she had
was going to be taken away from her
and she wouldn't see him again for the rest of her life
The way I talk, so extensive and spacious
it can offer room, as with that spreading
blanket in Naples, even to my critics –
I don't mean to attack them at all,
I'm not comparing them to disgusting,
nimble little mice that are hard to catch –
what an exhausting and thankless task is theirs!
constantly hunting for all the faults and defects
in a book or a poem, knowing full well
that they understand what was in the author's
mind, his intentions when he started writing
far better than the poor author himself

and that they could have carried out the whole project
and brought it to completion in a far more beautiful,
shapely and expert way if only they had
sufficient time, seeing they are always
so busy evaluating and judging
what other people have written –
I think it will come as an absolutely wonderful
surprise for them to find themselves already included
in a piece they haven't had the chance
to see yet, rather than providing
a pitiful little afterword to be published
in a newspaper or some magazine or other –
Hector, for example, who once told me
(the pronouncements of my critics
will be transcribed in English here,
given that generally
it's the only language they use,
even when dealing with Gaelic texts,
if the truth be told, the greater part of them
can't speak anything other than English
but they don't consider that an obstacle
or a limitation – so many critics
were thoroughly grateful to Sorley because
he put nearly ever poem he wrote
into English, permitting many an expert and scholar
who didn't have the faintest notion of Gaelic
to proclaim out loud and deafeningly
their verdict on his poetry,
concluding, who is to say? that the poet
could have saved himself an immense amount of trouble
by making a leap forward, and writing down
each prompt he got from the Muse

in English in the first place –
would that not have been far more sensible?
lots of younger poets, who imagine
that Sorley's mantle fell out of the skies
right down onto their own shoulders,
the minute they finish a poem in Gaelic
cannot wait to put it into English
without being sure which of the two
they ought to be more proud of)
take Hector, he's bound to say another time
'You've got such an astonishingly
puerile sense of humour' –
and the famed, venerable professor
who announced in a radio programme
on George Campbell Hay's poetry
'Nobody can write poetry
in a language he didn't dream in as a child',
tossing like that into the wastepaper bin
all the poems Hay wrote in Gaelic
though from one end of his life to the other
the professor cannot read one single line of them,
regarding me, I'm sure he'll come out
with the same opinion – that sort of people
do without evidence or research,
no need of either, their opinions remain
just as steadfast and unchanging –
and Big Charlie, who was so diligent and productive
rewriting the works of Alexander MacDonald
and Duncan Bàn, incapable of mumbling
even one word of Gaelic, as he
disarmingly admitted – who would hesitate
to praise without scruple such admirable,

forthright honesty – what is he
going to say? Might he put this poem too
into English, without understanding
a phrase or a sentence of it, not concerned
in the slightest about meaning or content,
adding, as he did already
with the work of far more important authors
new passages which I never wrote
and don't have any intention of writing?
The way I talk, like when my grandmother
was already very old, and came to stay
in my parents' house, sleeping on the big
couch in the sitting-room, and refused
absolutely to close the door
because she got a little bit restless
anywhere that was cramped and enclosed,
besides which she was always afraid
of ghosts, nobody had ever seen
a ghost in the house, but maybe she believed
that her own ghosts were capable of following her
wherever she went – with the door open
you could hear loud and clear the monstrous
horrendously noisy way she snored –
you'd think they'd started
digging up the road in front of the building
with the incredibly huge machines they use
these days, or else that enemy air force
planes had suddenly arrived to bomb
the city – we were all at our wits' end,
adults and children equally convinced
they'd not get a wink of sleep during the night
but then somebody would start laughing

and little by little no one could hold out,
we were all laughing, and fell asleep
without realising how that came about
and in the morning, eating our breakfast,
all that was needed was for one of us
to look another in the eye, and the laughter
came back, and the old woman kept asking
what was the joke we were sharing
and not telling, keeping it hidden from her,
and after she went back home
the game we played in bed was to see
who could do the best imitation
of the terrifying din that emerged
from granny's little nose while she was sleeping
The way I talk that approaches its end
like sleep overtaking you little by little
you detect it here and there in your body
but maybe it's fragments of wakefulness
you are noticing, seeing nobody
can trace the onset of sleep
which is a sort of forgetfulness
similar to the tide as it regains
a beach, conquering it stealthily,
the waves breaking and retreating so similar
to the ceaseless in and out of your breathing –
every now and again you miss out on a wave
and all of a sudden you're amazed
to see how little sand there is left
the tide has reclaimed practically the entire beach
consciousness has forsaken each of your limbs
with the irresistible onset of sleep,
your thoughts go into exile, no way to tell

what sort of a sanctuary will welcome them,
they could be passengers on a boat,
that faint smudge on the horizon somewhere,
an imprecise mark at the sky's edge
while you are like a candle they've blown out.

English version by Shuggie McCall

Donal McLaughlin (translator)
THE MAN AND THE YOUNGER MAN
By Mahmoud Hosseini Zad

Translator's Note: Mahmoud Hosseini Zad is an Iranian writer and translator who, in 2013, was awarded the Goethe Medal for his services to German literature. He is the author of a trilogy of short story collections: *Siahy e chasbnak e shab* / 'The Leaden Darkness of Night' (2005), *In barf key aamadeh* / 'When Did This Snow Fall?' (2011) and *Asseman, kipp e aabr* / 'The Sky, Full of Clouds' (2013). The third volume to appear is, in fact, the *second* part of the trilogy but the story 'The Man and the Younger Man', originally the *title* story, offended the Iranian censors who, for five years, refused to grant permission for the book. The story was translated using Mahmoud's own German version of the original.

Late. They arrived late.

They'd been about to depart when the pilot discovered a technical problem and it was another two to three hours before they were ready for take-off again.

As they waited to leave the plane, the man anticipated a warm breeze embracing them, like last time. Instead, a quiet but cold wind had blown on the steps, cooled the skin on their hands and faces, then blown off again.

The man had looked around. On the dark mountains, far in the distance, was still snow that shone in the moonlight.

They made their way to the hotel.

When they got out of the taxi outside the hotel, it was already midnight.

The man had reserved a room with a view of the garden.

The room was big. The long narrow window with light blue curtains looked out onto the large inner courtyard, its green garden. In the room were two beds. Separate beds.

The younger man was in the shower and the man, at the window. The lights round the large rectangular pool were on. Trees were casting heavy shadows. In one corner, in the semi-dark shade of a tree by night, sat two dark figures on either side of a table.

The man at the window could sense the silence between the two.

A waiter was clearing the tables.

The wind was slight yet the branches and leaves showed no resistance.

The younger man came out of the bathroom and, half-wet still, threw himself onto the bed at the window. The man waited. Waited, hoping the younger one and he would push the beds together. He waited briefly and then went into the bathroom. When he returned, the younger man was in a deep sleep.

He wasn't snoring, but purring like a cat having its head stroked.

Next morning, the room was bright. Still in bed, the younger man turned onto his side slowly, away from the bright sunlight falling on his face. His eyes closed still, he said, 'Could you close the curtains? And go on down. – I'll follow.'

The man closed the curtains and left the room.

The green of the trees and ornamental shrubs was a soft glowing green, and in the sunlight that fell at an angle into the garden, butterflies were fluttering round geraniums, oleander, acacias and lilacs. A pleasant scent, tangy and mixed with the smell of the damp earth, was hanging in the air.

The deep pool was empty. The only water was at the bottom, rain that had gathered in the night. The water was mirroring the silvery-blue sky.

The man greeted the hotel manager who told him breakfast would be served by the pool.

The tables in the shade on the other side were all taken. On this side, in the sun, the chairs were all free.

The man sat down at a table that was half in the sun.

The younger man arrived, sat down and said what a deep sleep he'd had. 'I didn't wake once!'

The man said, 'No, not once.'

The younger man asked whether he'd a sleepless night again.

The man smiled and didn't answer.

The waiter brought breakfast.

The man had ordered fried eggs too. The younger man, when travelling, liked fried eggs for breakfast.

The younger man cleared his plate. The man always liked to watch the younger man eat, with the kind of appetite he himself never had. The man cut off some of his eggs, put them on the younger one's plate. The younger man nodded and continued eating.

When he was done he asked, 'When do you have to go?'

'The meeting's at ten.'

'How long will it be?'

'Two to three hours for sure. You know what they're like, the way they haggle and bargain.'

The younger man laughed.

'I know what you're like!'

'It's my profession.'

They fell silent. Then the man asked, 'What are *you* going to do?'

The younger man said he'd go back to bed, having nothing else to do.

His head and shoulder were now in the sun. In this light, his eyes were more grey than green.

He'd then asked the man what he planned to do with the hour before the meeting.

The man had pursed his lips, raised his eyebrows, shaken his head and then watched the bird beside the rain at the bottom of the pool. Its bowed head twitched to and fro, like it was looking for its reflection. Rays of sunlight were hitting the water and it was as if the bird was resting by a silver pond.

The younger man had gone and the man hadn't noticed.

He signed the bill the waiter had left on the table, got up and walked through the garden.

The narrow paths between the flowerbeds and trees were laid with old bricks – yellow ochre and still wet.

The man stood in the shade of a weeping willow. As he took a deep breath, inhaling the scent of the gillyflowers still in the air, he heard a woman laugh. At the window of one of the upper floors, a man was standing smoking, his upper body naked, hairy. His left hand was reaching behind him, someone was trying to pull him back in. The hairy man smiled, contented, said something into the room and the woman giggled. He threw his cigarette out the window, closed the curtains and the woman screamed.

The man returned to the hotel, entered the reception area, intending to head upstairs, then stood for a while on the bottom step before retracing his steps, through reception, and leaving the hotel via the garden and a long corridor.

Out on the street, the sun was brighter and warmer.

The younger man was waiting at the window of a department store, opposite the hotel.

'I thought I'd accompany you a little.'

'Didn't you want to go back to bed?'

'I'll have time for that later.'

And he smiled.

They'd walked along the pavement on the right – in the shade. The warm breeze the man had expected at the airport the night before was now blowing in his face.

Two hours later, the man walked back to the hotel, again in the shade, this time on the pavement on the left.

The younger man was in the dining room.
    'I was in the toilet when you phoned.'
    'And you didn't answer?'
    'No need. I knew it was you. And thought I'd wait for you here.'

In the afternoon, they stayed in the room and lay on their beds. The younger man had slept all morning and was now unable to sleep. He talked, telling story after story, showing no sign of stopping. He told the man about his beloved grandparents, about his grandmother's house with the many many staircases, about the fat black cat his mother spoiled.

    The man had heard it all before, several times, but always enjoyed hearing it.

    With the younger man's voice in his ear and his eyes fixed on the ceiling, his eyelids started to get heavy and the ceiling, to float. The ceiling descended gradually and the voice of the younger man drifted off, became more distant, reached his ear from afar, then came closer again. His voice was now quiet, and later, the man couldn't remember when, and between which dreams, a familiar quiet voice had called him, a familiar smell had entered his nostrils, a familiar hand caressed his hair and his face, and a familiar warmth cloaked his body.

Water splattering in the shower wakened him.
    The window was open and the curtains were swaying in the slight wind, the wind bearing the pleasant, tangy smell of wet bricks and watered flowerbeds.

They got changed and left the hotel – on foot.
    The bazaar was long, loud, colourful. The air, heavy and spicy. They made their way through with difficulty. The younger man

said spices, the smell, always made him feel sick, he loved being in crowds though, walking through one.

The bazaar led to a large round space. Opposite the exit was the entrance of the mosque.

The younger man asked, 'Is that the mosque?'

Inside, they stood in the cool half-dark of the prayer room. The only light was falling from an opening at the top of the high dome. Glazed tiles – green and turquoise, saffron and pink, light brown – and the occasional black line and flecks covered the walls and dome. A glazed garden stretched from the tiles on the floor to the edge of the dome. All the way round the large circular chamber grew the thin trees and shrubs – the trunks, stalks, boughs, branches, leaves and blossoms – of a huge garden.

Freeing themselves from their roots, the trees and plants took off in every direction: chasing one another, looking for one another, rolling and running as they looked; clutching at one other; overtaking; glancing back before rushing ahead. Here and there, birds were sitting on boughs and branches. Here and there too, small patterns – intricate, square – blocked the way and this yellow, blue, turquoise, upward-flowing waterfall had to veer slightly before continuing its way up to where the birds were flying again, to the still looking-chasing-rolling-clutching leaves, flowers, boughs, branches. Reaching the dome, they swayed, twisted, turned, bowed their way to the top where they lay down round a bright dot in a tight embrace.

The younger man stood off to the side, wanting to leave. There was nothing more to see. He glanced round, looking for the man, and found him standing before one of the walls, as if mesmerised, hypnotised, the slow unconscious movements of his head following a bird on a bough right at the bottom, that held its head up, beak up, to look at a flower, then – bough by bough – flew up after the flower. With slow unconscious movements of his head, the man followed the bird like he needed to know whether the bird would fly all the way to the top, to the plants embracing round the dot; or whether, tired of flying, it would stop on the way up somewhere and watch the others fly by.

They went back through the bazaar, shopped at the large market on the square.

Evening had suddenly arrived. It was dark now. They took a seat in a small restaurant by the river. The water was sluggish as it flowed past, the reflections of the lights stretching into the deep green.

On the way back to the hotel, the younger man again spoke about happy memories, about their mutual friends, about his work, and occasionally took the man's hand in his, briefly.

They sat by the pool. The lights along the walls of the hotel garden were on. The trees were casting their heavy shadows into the centre of it, into the pool. There was a breath of wind and the shadows stirred.

They were drinking beer and the younger man said they'd walked for a long time and he was hungry. He laughed.

The man asked did he want his fried eggs already?

The younger man laughed again, said there was a time for everything.

A breeze that smelt of lilac wafted through the garden.

The man opened the curtains. Weak light from the garden fell into the room and the curtains cast huge shadows on the walls and ceiling.

The younger man came out of the bathroom and, with the white towel round his hips, stepped onto the balcony.

The man went into the bathroom, took a deep breath, inhaled the steam in the air, wiped the steamed-up mirror and studied his damp palm before slowly rubbing his face with it.

He turned on the tap, let the water run till it was cold, and got under the shower.

When he came out of the bathroom, the room was in darkness. The lights in the garden were no longer on. The quiet wind outside made its presence felt, bringing with it the tangy scent of the plants, and bearing away the purr – the purr of a cat having its head stroked.

In the morning, the room was again bright. The younger man asked the man to close the curtains.

Not getting an answer, he opened his eyes.

The other bed was empty. Untouched.

The younger man lifted his head, looked round, called the man two or three times, got up, checked to see was he in the bathroom, then went to the window.

The green of the trees and ornamental shrubs was a soft glowing green, and in the sunlight that fell at an angle into the garden, butterflies were fluttering round geraniums, oleander, acacias and lilacs.

The bricks were wet.

The chairs, all free.

Sitting at the bottom of the empty pool, beside the rain that had gathered in the night, was the man, his bowed head moving to and fro, like he was looking for his reflection.

Rays of sunlight were hitting the water and it was as if the man was resting by a silver pond.

Robbie MacLeòid
AUTO-FILIDH

tha mi . . .   sgìth
                   de luchd na Beurla
                   's mi leam fhìn lyrics
      duilich
      làn
      sunndach

tha mi an . . .   dòchas
      dùil
      Dùn Èideann

nach eil . . .   Beurla agad
      thu gam thuigsinn
      Beurla agad
      wifi ann
      Beurla agad
      thu airson ionnsachadh
      Beurla agad?

a bheil . . .   thu gam thuigsinn
      thu ann
      an taigh beag, càite
      Gàidhlig na cànan marbh
      thu fhathast ann?

dùthaich . . .   nam beann, nan gleann, 's nan gaisgeach
      nan Colonels
      Alba, a bheil i na
      nan Cruithneach, Asterix ann an
      translation for tattoo
      MhicAoidh

dè tha . . .   dol
                   romhad
                   thu ag ràdh
                   thu a' ciallachadh
                   gort
                   ceàrr orm?

dè . . .   an t-ainm a th' ort?

Callum McSorley
ON THE PLATE

The stars were getting closer. Paulina didn't need to take measure-
ments, she could see it with her own eyes. Every night when she
stepped onto the terrace, the warm, quiet air in harmony with the
gentle bob of the deck being lapped by the waves below, she could
see they were getting bigger. Nearer. And why doubt your own
eyes? That's what she always said to her followers. It had become
one of her catchphrases but that made it no less true.

The stars were getting closer, and that meant one thing: the
water was rising.

'What are you thinking?' Mike came up behind her – his
movement causing the house to stir against its moorings – and
slipped his hand onto her waist.

'Just that . . . it's amazing how beautiful a lie can be.'

His hand fell away. 'You should be recording, that's a good line.'

Paulina said nothing, pretended she couldn't hear the door
sliding shut as Mike went back into the house. He'd been acting
like a bitch since the whole Russian deal started. He'd blustered
some crap about it being unpatriotic but Paulina knew when he
was filling airtime with whatever flotsam churned up to the top
of his brain – they'd spent a lot of time on camera together, she
could tell he was vamping. No, he was afraid. It would be a hard
journey – a long one, and dangerous once they reached the ice
flows of the rim – and despite the swaggering, hard-edged truth-
rebel persona he wore on screen and at the conventions, Mike was
soft. It was one thing talking about going out there, another to
actually do it. And now the money was in place, Paulina was going
to do it.

'God willing,' she said to the firmament, knowing it was all
false, just the inside of a fancy glow-in-the-dark cloche over the
world. She scribbled into the notebook she kept in her pocket.

*

P: Tomorrow we cut the moorings and set sail!

M: We are Antarctica bound, baby! Yeehaw!

And there's the mask back on, Paulina thinks, the petted lip she's had to put up with over the last month totally gone. Asshole.

P: So long, SoCal!

M: Time to journey south, as the Globists would have you believe.

P: Go west, more like! Now, it's a straight shot from here to the Antarctic ice wall, but as you all know, with the ice melting and flowing inwards, it's almost impossible to navigate those currents with a straight heading, so we're gonna be moving almost in a zig-zag, riding the waves—

M: Tubular!

Mike is holding his arms out as if balancing on a surfboard; Paulina shrieks with authentic-sounding laughter.

P: So it's gonna take us some time to get out there. We don't know exactly how long but we've got provisions to last us, well, let's say we've got provisions for our provisions, we're ready for the long haul.

M: Also, we're already foreseeing trouble with the US Coast Guard. They – the government – well, they are not gonna want us going out there to the ice wall.

P: They *do not* want us going out there. Absolutely not. Not only will it prove the ice *is* melting—

M: You know, the world's top scientists have been saying this for decades – even among the Globists – they've been saying the ice is melting.

P: They call it *Global* warming.

M: They've always got to get the Globe in there somewhere. But they have been saying the same thing.

P: Yeah, and you know, our president may not want to believe it, and many of you watching out there don't want to believe it either, but the ice *is* melting. And you don't need any fancy experiments to prove it, you can see it plain as day with your own two eyes. Or plain as night, I should say. Me and Mike live here on what I like to call our *floabile* home—

M: That's a floating mobile home.

P: —and when you look outside at night you can *see* that the stars—

M: The lights of the firmament.

Asshole.

P: That's right, the lights of the firmament, are getting closer because the water levels are rising and pushing us up towards them. That's what you call empirical evidence right there.

Mike lets out a deep breath, shakes his head a little.

M: You gotta understand the consequences of that. It's scary. What are we gonna do when the water level reaches the ceiling?

P: Yeah, yeah, cause there's limited space here. The firmament, the sky, whatever you want to call it, is like a lid over the world. If the Earth's a plate, then the sky is a fancy glow-in-the-dark cloche. The water can't drain anywhere, so . . .

Paulina shrugs, her palms turned up flat, her mouth pulled thin in a half smile that says, 'Whatcha gonna do?' – a familiar gesture to her followers.

M: Take a deep breath, right?

P: It's not good, but it does give us an opportunity. The ice wall is melting and crumbling, right? So we can finally get up close to the face of the sky dome, check the tide line, see how much it's risen.

M: It's gonna be like the scummy water marks on my bathtub back in college.

P: Gross! I'm glad I didn't know you back in your college
        days . . .

*

They'd met through the forums, came face to face at conventions, crossed paths on the speaker circuit. They guested on each other's shows then eventually launched one together. Behind this, something was bubbling away, year on year.

Paulina thought they were too old to get married now, but Mike asked so she said yes. The ceremony was small, just Mike's folks, Paulina's sister-in-law with nephews in tow, and a few dedicated faces from the community who'd driven all the way out to the west coast. They had dinner at a Red Lobster, the sister-in-law smiling nervously and keeping the conversation focused on the kids, Mike's parents happy to oblige, eager to avoid looking at the three strange men, each one dressed in an awkward combination of overly smart and overly casual, all of them conspicuously unattached.

Afterwards, they drove down to the bay where Paulina was anchored. Mike, in his forties, had never lived outside the family home. He waited by the car, frozen before the gangplank, embarrassed by his one suitcase. Paulina took him by the hand.

The floabile (Paulina had specially prepared a drawer in the bedside table with condoms and Dramamine for Mike) was buoyed by recycled plastic bottles – great big nets stuffed full of them. The decks of the terrace were repurposed shipping pallets, the house itself a patchwork of reclaimed wood, appearing like some overgrown treehouse shrouded in palms and wild, creeping plants. Black solar panels gleamed in the California sun.

The environmental stuff had made Paulina a target. The community wasn't big on climate change. They accused her of buying into liberal media bullshit, or worse, that she had deliberately infiltrated the group in order to spread these false ideas. They demanded her birth certificate and she obliged. Mike posted his too, in solidarity, alongside their newly minted marriage papers. Work and love were tangled.

They settled into a steady routine of writing and filming broken up by meals and domestic chores. Mike was surprisingly fastidious, which suited Paulina, who had been living alone a long time and liked things a certain way. The first six months felt like a trial run, like any day Mike might be sent away for some infraction. But he wasn't. He stayed on and their following grew along with the clumsy intimacy between them.

*

P: *So*, we've hit trouble already.

M: As expected.

P: We were ordered back to shore by the Coast Guard.

M: The United States Coast Guard. Government agents. It's important to remember where the pay cheques come from.

P: Absolutely. These are soldiers, they came at us in their speedboats with guns and handcuffs and pepper spray and what all else . . .

M: Tasers and smoke bombs. You could see they were eager – absolutely *desperate* – to get into some sort of physical confrontation with us.

Mike nearly shit himself when they came aboard. Paulina did the talking. She stated their mission – it was public knowledge – but didn't say anything about the Russian-funded icebreaker they were due meet out of Ensenada. Not even her followers knew about that. As well as clearing the path through the ice flows, the icebreaker would be a lifeline if the ocean got choppy. Russian money had kitted the floabile out with some powerful motors but that didn't make it a boat.

P: We just put our hands up, told them we were on a peaceful and *lawful* mission. You know, this is a peaceful movement, a peaceful community, and I'm proud of that. Some people,

> if they knew what we knew, would be storming the
> corridors of power—

M: Taking up arms.

P: —in order to get them to tell the truth. But we're doing this by education and scientific experimentation. The results will speak for themselves.

M: If we can get to them.

P: We will. We'll find a way. I promise you all that.

The zeal is in her eyes.

*

'Of course I called the Coast Guard! Wasn't I supposed to?'

'What the fuck are you talking about!?' Paulina held fistfuls of hair, nails gouging into her scalp.

Mike's face was red. He paced around the kitchenette, Paulina and the argument following him round and round. The house was too small. He picked up a glass and filled it with water – pumped through the filtration system – and gulped it down before he answered. 'I thought . . . I thought that was the plan.'

'The *plan?*'

'Yeah, you know, we try to go out there but we get stopped from going by the Coast Guard – we fought the law and law won.'

'Why would we *want* to get stopped by the fucking Coast Guard!?'

'You can't be serious, Paulina.' Mike started his second glass of water. He tried to sound incredulous but failed. 'You don't really want to head out to Antarctica in a . . . in a floating shed.'

'A floating shed . . .' Paulina flapped her arms down to her sides then folded them over her chest, her voice going flat. 'A floating shed. This is my home, it's not a fucking shed. My *home.*'

'Our home.'

'Don't start that.'

'What?'

'You know what. This isn't about that. This is about you sabo-
taging the mission.'

'You mean the suicide mission.'

'If that's what it takes.'

'What? That doesn't even make sense, Paulina. Look, this was
a stunt. That's what it was, what it *always* was. Bring in the views,
go viral, whatever. A publicity stunt.'

'Not to me, Mike.'

'You wanna go and die out there in the cold?'

'This is the chance of a lifetime!'

'*There's nothing there!*' Their eyes locked. It took a few seconds
of silence for Mike to comprehend what he'd just let slip. Paulina
stepped back, her hand groping for the kitchen sideboard. In a
wild flash of adrenaline anxiety, Mike thought she might go for
a knife on the draining board. Instead she slid down onto the
floor, her back against the cabinet.

Her voice was quiet: 'Why? Why would you . . .'

'I love you, Paulina. Please, you have to believe that. That's
true, if nothing else.'

' . . . If nothing else . . .'

*

Mike liked the community, liked the attention they gave him, liked
having people listen to him even if he didn't believe a word of what
he was saying. It was a chance to be important, to feel like life was
exciting in a world where you'd worked at the local grocery store
for the last twenty-five years and still lived with your parents. Here
was another place, where you were in on a great secret, unravelling
a vast conspiracy, hunted and hunting.

The community was friendship, a sense of camaraderie, a noble
fight against the powers that be, even if that fight looked ridiculous
from the outside. They were his people, and he was their champion.

Watching him standing there on the dock in the dark – wondering,
no doubt, how he would get home by himself – as she floated out

to sea, Paulina decided to let him keep it all. She wouldn't say anything if he didn't.

The stars twinkled, hanging low – lower than ever – in the flat, black sky above. Just because it's fake doesn't mean it's not beautiful, Paulina reminded herself.

*

P: Now unfortunately, Mike has had to leave the expedition. He has some important family matters to deal with and can't go on. It's gonna be hard . . .

She takes a breath.

P: . . . It's gonna be really hard without him. Yeah . . . Communication could be difficult for a while, the further out to the rim we get – I get . . . *But*, I'll speak to you as soon as I can. My love to all of you watching, have a good night, or good morning, wherever you are on the plate.

*

Mike was back living with Maw and Paw when the news broke. He tried to call but couldn't get through.

Susan Mansfield
GARDENER

That's how I see my father, looking back,
always stooped with a spade in his hand
slicing square sections from the rich, dark earth,
the rhythm of it, the heft of each cut,
leaving it furrowed and fresh, full of promise,
the mica gleam of it, ready for growing,

ready for roots. For the magic of growing
happens deep down where the land gives back
the lifeblood to the seedling, promising
fragile new things which need tended by hand,
and some will wither, such is the cut
and thrust, the mixed blessings of the earth.

My father claimed as his this patch of earth,
set aside plenty of ground for growing,
how he paced it out, how the sod was cut
without ceremony, how he bent his back
to building a home with his own hands,
with enough room in case the promise

in her eyes became more than a promise
and tending his seedlings in the dark earth
was just the beginning. How one small hand
changes all you know about growing,
the unflinching force of it, no looking back,
eyes on the wide horizon ready to cut

and run, but all so soon, the toughest cut
for man or gardener, seeing a promise
fulfilled by leaving you, then going back

to lay down next year's crop in the mulched earth
and wait for the consolation of growing
while the furrows deepen on your gnarled hands.

I wasn't even there to take his hand
at the last, which is the strangest cut,
holding the phone in the half-light, the growing
sense that the things we think are promises
are only good intentions, and the earth
receives everything but gives nothing back.

Now, the weeds grow thicker and in my hand
no spade to cut them. I made no promises,
feeling the turn of the earth at my back.

Mina Moriarty
INHERITANCE

    cracks on my palms
read like a map
      quivering roads / thick clay voices / washing skirts in
          rivers

I chew these plumes of memory
let them dry in the   contours of my cheeks
smear wet sand into my thighs to become
trodden earth
let the weight of you press gently
into my ley lines

Siobhan Mulligan
SALMON RUN

I am pulled to the river by the hook in
my teeth. Swans, herring gulls, flick
of a cormorant, a bridge in lunular arch:
write down each. No vein of iron, no piston
to pump. My grandmother
would have avoided this. Her lungs
would swallow smoke as

salmon swallowed sewage, slag and
oil, steel and cistern smell, home settling
in choking gills. Years combed the water
into river again, but cycles stalled.
Rewilding required.
Now they swarm in shattered
patterns, fins glinting like
slicked stone.

Taste calls them on the currents:
the delicate peat of their hatching stream.
Generations flick past like calendar pages:
salt, smoke, citrus scent, calling me
like a dream.

Valerie Nieman
HEALING POWERS

From **The Women: A Solo Journey Through Scotland**

BURGHEAD, SCOTLAND – I kneel on a patch of earth at the foot of a cow pasture on the coast of Morayshire, the North Sea improbably blue behind me. I can hear water pouring under a square metal grate, which has a couple of metal cups chained to it. This is St Aethan's Well.

Reaching into the stone-lined chamber, I catch a cupful of water. It does not taste of anything, not minerals nor magic. The woman behind the counter at the Post in Burghead told me I'd find this well on the path back from Lossiemouth, close by 'the maltings', a giant industrial complex where Diageo steeps and roasts barley into the malt that becomes Scotch whisky at distillers all across the country.

'Drink from the well and your ills will be cured,' she said. 'It's safe, we've all drunk of it.' A stranger needs to be reassured, *this will not harm you.*

But cured? Why am I here, my back warm in the blessed north-eastern sun after so many days of rain, drinking from a well linked to an ancient Irish missionary? I'm neither Catholic nor a believer in the efficacy of sacred water.

'*St Aethan or St Aidan as he is also known was a follower of St Columba in Iona in the 7th century. He brought Christianity to the northern Picts and is the patron saint of Burghead. The water from the well comes from a spring higher up the hill and was thought to have healing powers.*' So reads the sign posted by the Burghead Trust, which cleared and reopened the holy well not long before I happened by.

I take another sip. Don't we all seek healing? I could count places in need of balm – rheumatoid arthritis that has been medicated to a low growl, gnarled feet, astigmatic eyes. The soul ache is harder to define.

I had only the haziest of reasons for this journey, saying that I hoped to do research for a long-delayed novel. But in fact, I was running. My marriage had come apart in ugly fashion. My mother had died, and not easily. I was free, now, and running from her death as I had spent decades running from her life, the destiny I had seen all around me as a girl. Grow up, marry a neighbouring farmer or factory hand, make a home, have children, fatten and slump toward death. I was so afraid of the traditionally female life she had chosen that I could never really see her – as a woman with a sharp eye, a storyteller's gift, and a venturing spirit, traits I'd inherited without crediting their source.

She was gone, reduced to ashes and fragments of songs and sayings that paced my steps. But my mother would keep reappearing, like the gods and goddesses who put on human form to walk among us. Women met along my solitary path taught me, cheered me, and occasionally saved me. A turn of phrase, a bright glance, and that stranger would shimmer with my mother's spirit for a second.

A lot of miles would pass under my brown ECCO trainers before I came to kneel at St Aethan's well. I set out from Fort William to walk nearly eighty miles across the narrow waist of Scotland to Inverness. After that, a long train trip north and a pair of ferry rides to the Mainland of Orkney and then the furthest Orkney island, North Ronaldsay, home to arctic birds and an ancient lineage of sheep. I walked and walked, through the Highlands, across the wind-battered hills of far islands, and now Moray. As many miles lay ahead, until I would stand on the beach where St Columba landed with his missionary brothers. By the time my peregrinations were finished, I would have put my hand on holy stones, drunk from wild-flowing burns, seen noctilucent clouds flame the northern skies. I'd have left behind quite a few pounds, one pair of pants, and the fear that I wouldn't be able to travel so far, so alone.

Here at the holy well, I fling the last drops of water onto the sandy earth, set the cup back on the grate.

Healing? Insight?

Maybe just the wash of other waters on my boots, the space of a new sky.

Jeda Pearl

15 WAYS OF LOOKING AT A TUAREG PENDANT

After Raman Mundair's '15 Ways of Looking at a Silk Sari'

1

a continent of silver,
cool, in your palm

2

hidden language, engraved in plain sight
a whisper of activism
in silver

3

sacred geometry, handed son to son
lost-wax silversmiths, hammer each amulet

4

on camels, indigo men rock
through storming sands,
regal pendants clapping their chests

5

mum gifts you a silver Tuareg cross
– not religious – a map-mark of home
to keep sons safe

6

onyx beads roll at your neck
threads rooted, pendant to clasp,
to pendant

7

precious metal anchor
crosses the Atlantic with you,
tugs your route home

8

brothers, skin stained from indigo,
sail on the Sahel's tides –
pendants clink as they laugh

9

Tuareg man, unpaid,
wears an Iferwane cross
inside Gold Coast yellow
magazine pages

10

under indigo dress,
cold silver warms on your breast:
hidden pendant

11

brown thumb lingers
on silver nubs –
borrowed pendant

12

Erykah Badu's soundwaves vibrate
120° 120° 120°
your ankh claps your chest

13
four silver stars light an indigo sky
the farthest four corners of the world
sunrise, sunset
home

14
made by their hands, unmake yourself
– taliswoman reclaimed

15
kiss cool silver to lips
breath of life
amulet

Sharon Gunason Pottinger
WALTZING WITH MORPHEUS

Your skin growing waxy like an apple
preparing for a long winter. Heart and lungs
pumping a rosy pink beneath the pallor
leaving no reserves for a return trip.

The little window in the door into the room
that has been your life for three years
conjures more of dying than the life you led.

I blink my eyes and think of how you'd like to be
not lying in this bed but dancing perhaps
so I listen for the music only you can hear,
a slow waltz with the king of dreams.

The waltzing stopped this morning. I console myself
imagining you with the wolf in his hour
on the far ridge between daylight and dark
in his good company slipping softly into the shadows.

Meghan Purvis
CORRESPONDENCES

On Reddit you can Ask A Mom, a forum of grown-up
      children
writing letters to mothers and getting answers, dozens of
      them,

not from their mothers: theirs are dead or estranged
or just beyond understanding, and so other mothers step in,

fingers pledging love and pride and listening. I wrote a
      poem, once,
for the boy of a family friend whose bed I slept in on holiday,

cartoon sheets and a lamp with a cartoon figure I didn't
      recognise.
I've lied: I wrote the poem for me, because of how badly I
      wanted

his warm light and his warm room. I left it under his
      mattress
hoping they'd never find it, that it would absorb into the
      half-bunk frame

like papier-mâché, wet and yielding until you find it's
      immovable.
Wind phones in Japan are that sort of quiet, or so I've read;
      you step into one

knowing no one will answer, but you talk anyway into the
      white noise
you think might hear. I'd like that, speaking knowing I was
      alone

but finding comfort from it anyway. The solitariness of it,
the not needing. A spiritualist years ago would accept letters
     to the dead

and answer them, unopened, words echoing the way some
     people say ghosts
work or are made of, these emotions with nowhere else to
     go. Edwin Booth

wrote to him. I lie again: he wrote to his brother, and we
     don't have the reply.
What could he have replied? The medium charged a dollar
     and three stamps.

Martin Raymond
LOCHAN NAN CORP

The Shepherd turns to the low stone hut, clears the snow from the plank door, shoves it open. Inside the dark intensifies and he feels for the wood, the rough boards somewhere down below his knees. He pulls, shuffling backwards, stooping out into the open, the winter morning.

The coffin is narrow, roughly made, something he can move easily. He's handled beasts that weighed more and were quick and lively, resisting. As he bumps it on to the sledge, he feels a displacement from inside. From his sack he pulls a tarry rope and corner to corner he straps the coffin down, tugs, knots, makes secure. The journey can start. There has been enough talk about this, enough whispering. It is now time to take her back to her people, to resolve this story that has consumed the village.

They gather. The Shepherd looks to the Minister. The Schoolmaster stands a little apart, head down. The two hired men, younger and glad of their fee, take up the harness. The Boy, almost a man, has begged to come. He takes up the rear. They make their way through the dark village. A few shawled women in low doorways, lit from behind by damped fires, watch them go, silently. They had judged already. The hussy. The hypocrite.

The six men follow the track to the west of the loch. The main road south on the far side has been blocked for days now at the pass, but here in the lee of the steep cliffs on this side of the loch the going is smooth and hard, the snow packed down by its own weight. Their footfalls in the dark squeak and crunch. The Shepherd is in front, but with one eye cast backwards to the Minister and the Schoolmaster, his betters, to assess their pace, to measure their aptitude. These are men accustomed to words not weather, men who do their work under roofs. They are already falling behind.

First light now, the darkness thinning out across the frozen loch. Even after weeks of frost there are open stretches where the currents keep the ice moving. The sky appears above them, the colour of slates on the kirk roof.

Now their journey properly begins, as they turn from the path up through trees, heading for the pass, into the hills. The Shepherd's thinking is the high ground will be swept clear by the winds. But first they have to win over this steepening ground. For the two men on the ropes, resentment rises up like their hot breath in the cold air. The snow in the forest is uneven, unsmoothed by the wind, peaking and troughing with treacherous hidden depths and concealed ice. There are falls, bone and skin are rasped, studded boots catch and clatter. The two men curse their burden. The Boy is silent.

The steep ground shortens the temper of the Minister and Schoolmaster, their hissed words rise up through the bare branches.

'She trusted us and now at the end you exile her, just a girl.'

'There is no other way. My conscience will not allow her in consecrated ground.'

'How can it be Christian to put her to this journey?'

'I will not be questioned in my conscience. In the schoolroom she was your responsibility. Your assistant. Look now to your own conscience.'

The words are no louder than the wind moving the tips of the trees far above.

'Her accident could not have been avoided.'

'Her *accident*, sir?' The Minister's voice like sliding snow, a small, hissing avalanche. 'How she got with child or how she drowned?'

The Shepherd hears it all, has heard it all, the gossip, the sightings, whether it was slip or jump and where the fault lies. But these things are natural to the village, part of its workings. It is enough for the Shepherd to get across this hill and back.

The trees begin to thin and the Shepherd is aware of two things
– how the wind is rising and what little distance they have covered,
the easy level miles of the loch-side stiffening into this slow struggle
up through the trees. And now there is worse. Before them the
ground angles up sharp and smooth, a white wall. The Shepherd
knows this slope well, beyond is flat ground between the two peaks,
a mile or so and then the descent. But the weather is coming for
them. The plateau is where the wind will funnel and will block like
bailiffs, pushing them back.

The Minister and the Schoolmaster are quiet now. They look
to the Shepherd, glad of this indecision, a moment to steady
their beating hearts, to suck in air, painfully chill. Five beards
are frosted, as if aged already by this journey. The barefaced Boy
is pale as bone.

'Gentlemen, I ask you to lend a hand here, to get behind to
push while we take the strain at the front.'

They work their way up the slope, a yard or two at a time with
the coffin suddenly an active foe. It has the promise of life again.
Gravity gives the dead heft, and, near the top, as the Schoolmaster
stumbles, the sled drops back against the slack of the harnesses,
slides as far as a half-buried rock where the Shepherd's knots,
corrupted by the cold, break loose and the coffin is adrift.

Quick as water, the wood slips over the hard snow. The men
watch. Only the Boy follows, tumbling in arcs of white powder.
The coffin goes fast into a sharp defile in the snow, shuddering to
a halt that snaps the long box upright. From inside there is a deep
thud, loud in the still woods. The Boy yelps like a struck animal,
his rolling fall takes him all the way to the coffin where he kneels
and embraces the rough wood. The men stare, nothing is said. By
the time they reach the Boy his face is dry. The Shepherd gives a
few instructions. They must hasten.

When they reach the plateau it is another climate, another
world. The wind has been waiting patiently for them, its tree-top

murmurings now a high shriek. The air is taken from them
before they can breathe it fully. They are aware of how far they
are from shelter. The light is changing, the snow brightening as
the sky darkens.

Frozen rain comes at them like birdshot. They lean into the blast
like pioneers. The boards of the coffin, low as they are, conspire
with the wind, thwarting. No talk now, breathing is hard enough.
Through the driven snow, under the low sky, between the shifting
outlines of the two bens, is the lip of the bealach, and then, beyond
the swinging, clanking gate of the wind, is the south slope, and
downhill to food and fire.

They walk on, each contemplating why they find themselves
here, exposed. For the Shepherd and the two men this hardship is
their usual work. The Minister and the Schoolmaster have their
own reasons. The Boy nurtures his silence.

Then, forming out of the snow, the lochan. Its ice swept clear, it
haunts the way ahead like a dark premonition. Though narrow, its
length stretches across their path. The far side of the lochan is no
great distance at all, but the wind and the snow make mock of
normal measures.

The Minister favours the longer route, anti-clockwise, across
rough ground but under the partial lee of the highest peak. The
Schoolmaster is for the shorter shore. Both fear the ice. The hired
men and the Boy are not consulted.

The Shepherd has had enough. His entire length is white to
windward. Only he can make this judgement. This is his world,
not the thin word-world of the other two. He points.

'Cross.' He looks to the Minister, the Schoolmaster. 'Straight.'

The Minister frowns down on him from his authority. 'It may
not hold us.'

The Shepherd stabs the ice with the iron spike of his crook, as
if to dispatch a broken gimmer.

'Look, there is no movement, it is frozen to its depths.'

The Schoolmaster questions, that is how he lives, questions, questions. 'How can you be sure? I for one will stay on the solid earth.' He has most reason to return her to her people, put his guilt behind him. Then home to his wife.

'As you wish, but you leave your portion of the task to the rest of us, and you travel the rest of the way alone, we will be far ahead of you.'

The Boy shivers. One of the hired men turns away, his back to the roar, and spits.

'We have no time for your . . . considerations.' The Shepherd speaks the word like a blasphemy. 'The darkness will take us.' He steps out on to the ice.

They watch him go, look one to the other, for one moment their eyes connect, the men and the Minister and the Schoolmaster and the Boy. Tugging the sledge, they follow. The going is fine, there is only a scraping of snow over the rough ice. Their iron-shod soles grip, the sledge bumps and slips across the level ground, even the wind seems given to a partial truce. They can begin to imagine the townships ahead, the mutton, ales, the fires. Boots ring solidly on the surface. But within a hundred steps they hear a noise, strange and deep, loud enough above the wind and the rasp of their breath. Under their feet, long white cracks stretch away forever. All stop except the Shepherd, he calls out with the wind over his shoulder.

'The ice is stretching. Breathing. Have faith, it can't harm you.'

They step forward as one, all of them, the four men and the Boy, trusting the sixth. Then the ice breaks into a great raft which overturns slowly, tips them all and closes like a black door above.

On the surface the wind booms on. Below all is glassy, silent and terrible. The swift business of dying consumes all six. Look down from the other world of sky and air, down through the twisted carnival mirror of ice and see the faces, wide eyes, clawing nails, mouths tight.

Below they dance as never before, turning, rolled on their heads. Their clothes, their boots, their Bibles, their money, their guilt, their confessions, their innocence, all pull them down to the mud. The water is not deep. It doesn't have to be. Only the Boy pushes upward, unburdened. The coffin floats just under the ice. He embraces it, arms all the way round, tighter than he ever hoped. He feels something like the pain he felt when he spied her with the Schoolmaster, deep in the summer bracken. His knuckles are raked by the underside of the ice but he clings on until the coffin fills and sinks.

*

Weeks later the wind finally turns to the south and in days of rain just the highest bens are left white, the grass on the lower slopes flattened and bleached. Word had come from her brother that the plot he'd dug in his own land was still waiting. He was a man of substance, sending his sister to train as schoolmistress in a hill parish should not have ended as it did. These people could not even bury her. With the speculations about her condition and whether she determined her own drowning, it should all have been over.

The village didn't need the brother's message to know what had been lost, but could only wait for a thaw. Why risk more lives to go up there and hack at the ice? But now in the warm air from a new season the remaining men go out, up the wet paths. A dreadful journey. The plateau is blasted by wind as always, the flattened grass stretches towards them, rippling like a live flank, but they push on towards the lochan.

At the north end, downwind, there are tangled heaps of old ice, dirty and shattered. Amid it all, like six black rocks, six humps, each with its own intent hoodie crow, flying off only when they come within stoning range.

The retrieval of the bodies then the burials are long difficult tasks – they diminish the village. Planting is late, a dry harvest is missed and in the vindictive autumn rain more is lost. It is not the absence of men – villages of women generally prosper – but it is hard to go forward in the lee of such hard fortune. There is disease, there are deaths, there are dispersals to relatives, to mills, to cities, into another century and with each re-telling the real story wears away until it is gone. Just the stones remain, in snow and in thin sun, above the pale spring grass.

Lotte Mitchell Reford
BLAST ZONE

I want to write about meaningful things
but everything coming out is about fucking
or sometimes about churches. Often about how
I'm worried about drinking myself stupid
or to death. There is a story I've been wanting to tell
about the time I broke my leg and the morphine barely
        worked,
how a man who loved me held my calf for an hour and felt
        the split bones
pressing into his palms, and also a scene stuck bouncing
        round my brain,
something I heard in an interview on NPR about nuclear
        tests
in the '50s and how they made young men bear witness to
        the devastation
and gave them questionnaires afterwards to gauge its effect
on their mental health. Was it like a psychiatric intake form?
'In the last week, on a scale of 1–7, how often have you
        thought
about death' – this one is always a 7 – or more like the
        pain charts
they give you in an ambulance. Those ones have faces
to represent 0, 1–3, 4–6, 7–10. The only time I have pointed
at one of those little faces I had to ask what I was comparing
my current pain to. *I've never felt anything worse than this*
I said, my left tibia and fibula smashed into several pieces,
But someone must hurt more? Like, where are those men
        now,
who after they watched the blast from a trench at a distance,
        walked out in a line,

a search party, and combed the desert for what was left.
Those bombs are used now to measure everything
temporally. There is a before and an after; for bones, for
      wine.
And in the middle of that hard dark line across time
were animals penned in the blast zone. The furthest out
      lost limbs
and survived a while. Most of the animals were pigs
because pigs die like humans, and the guy I heard
on NPR, he said the worst part was how delicious
the whole desert smelled, a giant barbecue,
and that as they are dying like humans, pigs scream like
      us too,
and yet, still, he thought of food. While we waited
for the ambulance Thom and I talked about pizza to
      distract me,
pretending I'd be home in time for dinner.
In the hospital they pulled on my foot to reset the bones
      above.
They told me not to worry because pain
is something we never really remember and anyway
I'd had all the morphine they could give me. I didn't want
      to point out
there are many kinds of pain, and some are hard to forget
some remain etched into you, your body and bones
or become a new kind of glass, Trinitite, superheated sand
which registers as radioactive. I didn't want to tell them
that I had a hefty tolerance for opioids.
I never want to tell people who fix bodies
about the things I do to mine. Most of those men,

young as they were, must be dead now. Our bones hold
the nuclear tests in New Mexico, and so do wine cellars,
              trees
and soil, but how do we hold those boys
with us too, how do we keep bearing witness,
how do we remember to remember?

Olive M. Ritch
LETTER FROM HOME, 1915

Dear Son, a very bad thing happened here on Sunday
        morning –
Dod o the Meedows shot himsael in his ain barn
and Florrie found him when she went in
for maet tae the horse.

He was gone tae bed at night, same as usual,
and she did not hear him go oot.
He only haed his bare feet
and draaers on.

I think a great peetie o Florrie
that found him.
                He was a very bad man
and he has made a very bad end.

Dod did not believe in God,
so you see when we are tae wirsaels
what puir things we are.

May God keep aabody in their right mind.

maet: food; ain: own; draaers: underpants; peetie: pity;
wirsaels: ourselves; himsael: himself; puir: poor; aabody: everybody.

Daniel Shand
OUR LITTLE PIECE OF HEAVEN

dear mum and dad and hanna too.

how are you? i am fine thanks. it feels like a big long while since i saw you and the father said i should write because time is running out. so this is it.

a little about me perhaps. well where to start? i suppose the main thing is that i am in charge of the chickens so how about that? it is an example of very great health to eat one egg a day so yes it is an important job, thanks. the chickens are called

> vera
> clucks
> little eggo
> darling

and more besides. let me tell you – these ladies love me. in the mornings i am running out with seeds and throwing hands of it onto the yard and darling and little eggo know the sounds of seeds falling so know this is breakfast and those ladies love seeds let me tell you. i have to come clean and say i get a little proud of myself seeing the ladies pecking their breakfasts and i know pride is a sin but its hard. another part is we sometimes get a fox in the nighttime – little reddish animal who has bad intentions and some nights i am sitting up with one of the fathers gun machines to be safe from fox – who we call

> dirtyboy

the ladies dont know of this – least of all little eggo whose head once got stamped by a truck – but they are safe from dirtyboy so thats the main thing.

what else. apart from chickens and fox i am also in charge of helping sister joan on dinners. this is the worst let me tell you. sister joan is a nightmare from hell – bless me – and is very strict on dinners being done proper and correct. its not right to complain or shirk i know but sister joan is always twisting my melon about cutting the carrots right. batons is her whole deal. also with peeling the potatoes and using the small knife to take out the spuds eyes, which is a word i forgot and did a big laugh when sister joan said spuds eyes. she didnt care for my big laugh and said to show respect for the produce of the father.

i was like sorry sister joan my bad.

dinners are the main thing here. in the house is this long table and every one of us is sitting there at seven sharp for eating – one egg each, very great health – all of us hungering from our day of guarding chickens or other employment. first comes prayers by the father then eating sister joans dinner which i have to swallow without breathing because of taste. after dinner we go to the play room to lay with each other but i wont write that. then its personal reading before bed. for me now i have struggles with full books. only the god almighty can say why but pictures are best for me anyway. my favourite is the one who is called

rupert bear

mum and dad. can i tell you something? i am like not at all missing the city. no way. here there is no other buildings apart from the house and other family buildings and it is so excellent. from the hill you can see down to the water – which yes is very sparkling – and to Main Land across. hardly any cars come past which is great health because of pollution and fumes. remember once in the city when i was young and boys almost stabbed me and took away my phone and so on. well here there is no phones and no boys so i am safe from stabbing – bless me.

a new bad thing is that some men came from Main Land. they had on proper suits what none of us wear and we got this big lecture from the father at breakfast. he was like no speaking to these guys and go out and work like normal except no talking. the men came and looked at the house and other buildings and wanted to check our sewage piping. the father was walking with them and one of the ladies sort of shouted – i think little eggo (very outrageous) – and he gave me this look.

wow.

dad. i remember you giving me looks but they were cake compared to this.

ok coming clean i am a small part scared of the father now and then. fine i know he loves me with a fury and is my only chance of going to the pearly gates but man alive those looks. anyway. the men went off and the father slept outside to be closer to the god almighty. which also put a fear into me.

i suppose my best friend is brother samuel. brother samuel is young compared to me but his beard is longer. that is the style here. his main thing is the wood chopping because of his strength. he says to me – i am happy chopping wood because i am chopping up the universe with itself. i say i dont get this and brother samuel says the god almighty makes everything even wood and axes but only humans can use the universe against itself – the axe against the wood. ok ive been to college and had the Good Book read to me but man alive what does that mean? its sometimes hard for me to use my brain proper i must say. i forget about things like before or in-a-minute. brother samuel says the men coming and going was an ill omen. same for the father sleeping outside.

hanna. sorry. i forgot about you. how are you? you would be very pleased to see me now i think. i am skinny and no longer smoke or drink beers apart from the fathers special wine. you wanted this for wedding photographs but what can i say. the father says our sort of wedding was a damned sham and the only true connection is between all human minds. this is why we lie all together after dinners. with you and me there was just two of us and maybe this is why we were so cross. man alive i am sorry if i lost my temper. now i am always totally relaxed, let me tell you. this is what i hope for you too hanna. come here if you want to. you have to take the boat but whatever its cheap. i think youd get a real thrill off of lying with brother samuel and i would be like ok whatever.

i do sometimes wonder what everyone is doing since i left. i guess i never said goodbye and that seems strange now. goodbyes are important. since ive been here two sisters have left and they said goodbye by burning down one of the other buildings and swimming for it. this is what we call a grand gesture. it was a weird vibe but i got to look after clucks and little eggo and darling and vera so i was like fine by me. i suppose i wanted to say goodbye to you but let me come clean – i cant remember going. weird am i right? what i remember is meeting sister emily in this bar and she was like what makes you happy and i was like nothing and she was like thats a problem and then next thing i know i am beyond drunk on special wine and who knows how i get here. just the god almighty, am i right?

after the men from Main Land went and the father was sleeping 'under the stars' i got bad news from brother samuel. he says to me youll never guess what and i was like what and he was like i saw dirtyboy sneaking about in the back acre. man alive. i was like nightmare, brother samuel. it was actually basically ok because i was excused from dinner and play room and went to the bunks for an early nap. i snoozed all evening then had special wine and went in the dark with a gun machine to see if dirtyboy was coming back.

oh my god i didnt even say before. the best thing here is our stars and moon. man alive. mum i think you would get a real enjoyment from these stars and moon. i dont remember now if you liked them especially but all mothers enjoy gorgeous things so sort of picture the whiteness of toothpaste and you will be halfway to this crazy brightness. very great for hunting specimens like dirtyboy who i have never shot at but can scare away using loud swears. i waited on the gate of the back acre and did not see one whisker on his head for hours and hours. you might be saying to yourselves wow that sounds like a total yawnfest but let me come clean – it really wasnt. ever since ive been here i am never bored. i can be quiet for a whole day and still dont want to see television or scroll a mobile. weird am i right? now and then i get a little itch but special wine fixes it up good and proper.

just when i was going to say hang this and go back to the bunks for some illicit Zs someone whispers what are you doing out here son? i thought my poor entire body was going to pop! a voice from nowhere, i was like man alive.

then i see him.

it was the father standing behind me on the wiggly path. i said to him about dirtyboy and he told me it was good i cared about the ladies so much. that was an example of great compassion for all the god almightys creations. thanks i said. the father was seeming a little weepy to me but i was too scared to be like hey how are things sir?

he came over to have a sit on the gate too. he told me things were bad about the men from Main Land. he said what have i done thats so wrong apart from giving innocents the chance to reach the pearly gates. so what if some regulations are amiss. so what if some code isnt up to scratch.

i did not know what the father meant about this code but was like totally sir. that code is a piece of work.

he said to me time was running out on our little piece of heaven. meaning the farm and so on. he was like but come on wasnt it spectacular while it lasted? wasnt it the very kingdom on earth?

i was like yeah it probably was now i thought about it.

man alive this was the heaviest chat i had since sister joan caught me with my finger in the jam pot. here was the father of all people sort of crying beside me in the nighttime and here was me frightened and also feeling a special twist in my belly because it was me that was listening. me! amazing things probably happen every day in this world but this was the first of me knowing about it. i thought of all the other brothers and sisters over in the bunks and i admit that i left a door open for pride.

then the father was like im thinking of throwing a party. one last hurrah to see out the end of an era. lots of special wine for all and perhaps even a feast. you can imagine what i said. it was: wow that sounds nice.

he said but the thing is son is we will need to say goodbye to the ladies to prepare for the feast. the chicken ladies and the cow lady too. she is the one we call

mrs milk

and i was like thats really sad but they will understand if i tell them it smooth and nice. maybe throw out another hand of seed to sweeten the deal. thats the spirit said the father and we got off the gate like we were going to head back to the bunks when from my eye-corner i seen something moving. something reddish and sly.

it was dirtyboy watching us from down by the river and because of moonlight his eyes were these sneaky torches.

it was all like totally dark and still with dirtyboy seeing us. i whispered to the father: will i get him then? (even though i have like zero clue how gun machines work). i could hear the fathers nose breaths as he met eyes with dirtyboy and a long minute passed in that nighttime.

then the father said no. now there is little point, son.

so thats all the news i think. everything from then on has been party party party. brother samuel has been chopping down every tree on the farm. he has grown extremely muscular may i say. sister joan has been working night and day on meals and sides and a multitude of special wine and i broke the news to the ladies that they will soon graduate into chicken meat. the father said we should all write letters since we only have so much time. i have been working on mine for days and my hand is full of ache. i have also been doing some personal thinking about the farm and the father and the Good Book and some rememberings about when i was small and when i was married. thinking is hard for me but i have come to an idea that i want to share.

so listen mum and dad and hanna. the thing im getting to is this: you are the loves of my life, i promise. ok i went away by mistake and wont come back now and youve probably forgot me anyway but i know something. it is this: i am going to see you at the pearly gates! how about that? i can feel its true even though the father says normal folk wont get there. i am going to be flying around with my little wings and harp and mum and dad youre going to come up those steps and be so so proud. hanna we will still be married there but will also be married to all human minds. i am going to hold your hand softly and quietly let me tell you.

hallelujah. i can already feel my hair growing back!

in a minute i will give my letter to sister joan and it will go into a sack and be taken to the post office when she gets the boat to Main Land next. after that who knows. i cant remember now how post works. maybe i never knew!

please know i am watching you. i am still in my bedroom sometimes, in my heart.

love from son. from husband. hallelujah and goodnight.

Mark Ryan Smith
TEAM BUILDING

Session 1 (09:00–10:15)
We circle our chairs in the doughnut of new beginnings.
We visualise ourselves in the swamp of limitation.
We role-play our way through the snow-globe of fear.
We enjoy a swing at the piñata of innovation.

Session 2 (10:30–13:00)
We all take a turn on the motivation trampoline.
We land in the valley of workplace cohesion.
We explore the foothills of organisational efficiency and
We eat free sandwiches on the peak of Mount Achievement.

Session 3 (13:30–16:00)
We make sails from the pages of flip-charts and
We run them up the masts of our rafts of self-knowledge.
We round the Cape of Continuing Professional
          Development.
We anchor ourselves to the quaysides of change.

Kathrine Sowerby
WHOLE BLOODY ENDEAVOUR

I dream of a job painting
white lines on concrete
around a swimming pool
I want to mark out what matters
be busy

In the dream I am my daughter
the boss says there is no more work
lines do not need to be painted that often
would she like to try other work
delivering milk perhaps

Or I dream of feet turning into hooves
but I don't panic
think of the new-found speed
with which I will run

I thought we were going to have sex
do they still call it that
it's been such a long time
I can barely remember how it all works
but it's not complicated

Anyway now I have these hooves
you may not be at all interested

Richard W. Strachan
MERCURY

0

A photograph on the horizon. He blinks to miss it. A snapshot, like the sun is rising.

10

The forecourt is ringed with ochre dust, this dust that gets everywhere; into the eyes, into every fold of skin. There are spots and dark patches of evaporating water on the ground. Inside he can hear the boy, all the work he puts into breathing. He can hear the circling motors howl on the Jackass Flats, going nowhere. He puts his hand to the door; the metal is night-cold.

The boy lies on a cot in the corner of the room, the dormitory. He looks like an old man. He whispers in his sleep.

'. . . *es ist meine Mutter, und sie ist auf mich herab schauen . . . ah, Mutter, Mutter, bitte, mich wieder zu sammeln, sammeln, mich . . .*'

He wets a cloth and cools the boy's forehead, the water running down the wrinkles in his skin. Wrinkled, shrivelled like a nut, but he's no more than twenty-two. He was.

It'll get better, he says to the boy. It won't be long now. You just need more time.

He leaves the dormitory and crosses the park, past the twin parched tennis courts, the fragile scrub. Steel light blazes from the skin of each bungalow, each trailer and hut. The dust is a scattering against his feet.

He moves through the bar, eyes adjusting; the paused jukebox, the stuttering neon lamplight. Outside, Grigor sits under the awning amongst spent beer barrels and empty crates, a bottle in his hand. He stands next to him, both of them frosted in this dust, although he's done no more this morning than walk from one building to another.

How's our patient? Grigor asks him.

We need a doctor.

And what do you think a doctor will do?

He says 'doctor' the way some would say lawyer.

Then it's just a question of waiting.

Grigor drinks from the bottle. How can we wait, he says, when nothing changes?

9

In the vehicle shed he checks over the truck and drives out to the first gate. Again, rising to the back of his neck, is the grip that says, 'Don't go.'

The desert, molten, falls away in red and blasted green, patched here and there with stubborn cactus. The mesas in the distance may be no more than a bank of rising cloud, and the road stretches off in a single lane that curves to a point where the men who built it had eventually given up, leaving behind them a great spread of beaten metal and mounds of rucked tarmac.

He gets into the truck and drives. The sun is rising.

8

There's a point two miles from town where the ground dips into a shallow declivity, a natural amphitheatre. Stones and rocks litter the ground, each fixed in the same position for millennia. In the centre of the space there is a cleared area and six rows of wooden benches. All the metal in the wood, the domes of fixed screws and bolts, are dull as rust. It doesn't rain in this desert. The benches are bitten with rot, dry white flaking patches on the sides like psoriasis. The benches are lined up exactly, every row exactly spaced from the other, apart from the last. The last bench is thrown off true, skewed to the side, opening like a hinge on the block of benches. In the dust around the feet of the benches there are buttons, a watch strap, the unmoving silver foil strip from a stick of chewing gum.

7

He doesn't really believe it exists. He's never seen it, but then no one else has seen it either. It hangs there in his mind unconfirmed, bold as myth. It's a story heard at one remove, from a friend of a friend, from another worker passing through. There's no position on the map at which a confident finger can point.

It's real though, everyone swears so. He has the feeling that if you looked hard enough you would see it just at the point when you stopped looking. When you turned to leave, swinging open the dusty hinge of the truck door, your gaze would sweep to the right and you would see it there, stark, right in front of you. And still you wouldn't believe it. A fence, three strands of barbed wire stretching in a straight line for a quarter of a mile, freestanding, the fence now detached from whatever it used to fence in. You would look at it and see the fence, and then you would look again and not believe what you were seeing, because the wire strands are just hanging in the air with no posts to hold them up. The posts are long gone, blown to powder and dust, but the barbed wire remains – hanging there, vibrating, held by who knows what force or compulsion, a need inside the steel to cleave to its original purpose.

You'd see it and later maybe think about it, and you'd tell those who wanted to listen and they would pass the story on. Or they'd remember it themselves before they left, something that was still to happen, nagging at them like a guilty conscience.

But he doesn't believe the fence is really out there. He doesn't know anyone who's seen it, and even if he saw it himself he wouldn't believe. He'd just get back in the truck and head on home down the Mercury Highway. He would tell no one.

6

Grigor leaves one day. He gets back to the town and the bar is empty, and the hut where Grigor lives is empty too. He had nothing to take with him. All that he's left behind are the lost loves of his empty bottles.

He sits in the bar and listens to the modulating hum of the fridge, the persistent disappointment of the wind moving between the trailers, the harsh breath of the distant mesas. He had only just got here.

5

They drive up Jackass Flats Road. Time shimmers like a heat haze, melting up into the vast shield of blue. The boy hooks his arm from the window and when he draws it back the arm is sleeved in dust. One of them will say something, and an hour later perhaps the other will reply, answering a statement made the day before, or tomorrow, or the day after that. The boy chews gum – always chewing – and spits the gobbets out of the window. He imagines the gum patting solidly into the dust like stones, remaining undegraded in that position for a hundred thousand years. The boy throws away the silver strips of foil from the gum sticks, like a radar countermeasure. They drive on, north, into the rising sun.

While they work the boy finds a beetle in the dust, shining like petroleum, a rainbow smear across hard chitin. The boy watches it crawl to the tip of his finger, and, with an audible pop, the wing-case opens and the little scraps of polythene unsheathe. It vanishes into air, where it can't be followed. The boy watches it.

What is that, he says. In the language?

Beetle.

I know this, but what kind?

He doesn't know. He shrugs, as if to say all of them are the same; what matter the little differences.

Your English is getting better, he says to the boy.

I'm at the end of the book! Now, to learn everything from those I work with. Soon I will speak it just as good as you do. But you don't speak much.

No.

Grigor does. And his English is terrible!

This is true; Grigor's English is terrible, even though it is his first language. Here, many arrive who have it as their second or third. Passing through, working where no one wants to work, passing on when they have had enough. They'll all be back in time.

Miles above, a contrail pierces a bank of cloud, hanging there unfeathered, undiminished, maybe for a month or so. It's hard to tell.

Later, they drive out to the holding tubes. This is the worst job. He leaves it until the end of the day, when the sun is rising.

4

It's far out there, as near to the middle of the desert as could be imagined. From a distance it's just a patch of white against the rusty sand, but then, getting closer, it unfolds itself; a rhomboid shell of ceramic and steel, the skin painted in a non-reflective matt so thick it's like a covering of clay. Lunar-modular, a bunker, the windows are foot-thick slits of clear plastic, the door a bulkhead with a screw-wheel handle. The windows look to the east, the distant shadow of the mesas rising from the plain, the long strip of the Short Pole Line Road. Three wooden steps lead to the door, but the wood is all decayed. Next to it, an appendage, is a narrow wooden shed that looks like a beach hut, its sloping roof painted bright crimson. It has no window. Antennae sprout from the roof of the module; aerials, receptors, a circular dish. The shadow the module casts to the ground is fixed in the sand. No digging would ever disturb it. When the module is gone, the shadow will remain.

3

Standing far out on the abyssal plain are two spurs of steel, three storeys high. They're planted fifteen feet from each other. Around the base there's a patina of dust and the support struts are clothed in the rags of desert plants. At the base they stand straight, like pillars, but at the top they begin to twist and lurch away from true, the metal twisting, corkscrewed, splayed out west to reach across the desert. The steel has been unravelled; they are like blasted trees with their branches crazed against wide, unending sky. Listen, and in the rare wind passing through the open strands of steel comes a high, persistent whine.

Dusk falls fast in the desert, orange and cream and a last burst of crimson, but the stanchions reflect nothing of the setting sun. They fade into the darkness, and in the night they could be made of nothing more substantial than paper. Still persists that high, uneasy whine though, even when no wind is blowing. Red sand perhaps, striking the ribbons of steel, the wires of the burned platform, revealing themselves slowly in the morning when the sun is rising.

2

There's a new arrival one day, the first for many months. His name is Grigor, and he's dropped off at the gates with nothing but the clothes he wears. No rucksack, no kitbag or suitcase. The car that brought him screams off towards the road. Hours later he will see the car from the roof of his hut, still trailing a scarf of dust as it weaves through the desert, desperately looking for the way back. The circling engine howls all the way down on the Jackass Flats, the great table of the salt plain.

Grigor takes over the running of the bar and the canteen. He'll spend hours between jobs sitting in there, talking with Grigor, waiting for the boy. Something in the way Grigor occupies the space behind the bar tells him that he will be here for some time. The easy authority, the broad forearms resting on the bar top, makes him look too comfortable to move. He has come home again.

1

He goes out to the holding tubes at the end of the day, the worst job. He comes to a field of wooden posts, each as high as his chest and topped with a wire cage. He walks between them breathing through his mouth, opening the cage doors and sweeping out the dust from the compartments into separate polyurethane containers. He stocks these in the back of the truck. The dust gets in your eyes. He scrubs this dust from his face in his hut, and in the sink the runnels of water are black. He blows black dust out of his nose, he scrapes black dust from his ears. When he raises his head from the pillow in the morning the cotton is stained with a faint Shroud of Turin-impression of his resting face. The dust is under his nails, between his teeth.

The heat from the rising sun is deep in his skin, its burnished light, the insistent attention like a constant, monitoring eye.

He refills the cages.

o

The boy is dying, there's nothing they can do for him. He has phoned it in but no help would be quick or slow enough to reach him. He thinks of the call skipping down the wire, the wires strung out south across the desert in limp, sagging stretches, his voice diminishing towards the distant recording device. The wire could be cut a hundred miles from here and they would never know.

Who will listen to his voice speaking these words a thousand years from now? In what future museum are his words being played on a permanent loop, accessed through headphones and attuned to the recursive stock footage played endlessly on a big screen in a darkened room? He speaks them anyway. Somebody has to.

Even Grigor takes his turn attending. The old man who was once a boy has stopped talking in his sleep. Words have fallen away, sound has no more force of expression, and all that remains are vague head movements, faint twitches in the limbs, the mouth papping open and closed with a dry smack and no words. They hold the wet cloth to his forehead, though his skin is cool. They have no other gestures to make, and when the old man dies he will drive him out into the desert, to the holding tubes, to the skewed wooden benches, to the lunar module or the stanchions. Someone else will come through, in time. Time is all they have.

In his hut he washes the black dust from his face, and when he looks in the mirror it's like he's gained a decade, or lost a year.

A photograph on the horizon. He blinks to miss it. A snapshot, like the sun is rising.

Ojo Taiye
MOURNS DOWN THE MOON & DISSOLVES IT
ON HER TONGUE LIKE A WAFER

Bogoro Massacre, February 29, 2003

is there a lexicon for sadness? & between my mouth & drought,
                                    my body knows what it needs
                                    to burn. & to singe is the
                                    body's oldest creed.
                how do you un-love a motherland that chews
                                    & spits you out like a
                                    broken tooth?

                                    –

i know – once there were two brothers. or maybe two friends.
let's try again: once, there was Ituri. who came first?
                        Lendu or Hema

                                    –

                        i am not an annalist but i bind myself
                        with history, not just *Bogoro*.

            i am the son of a black tide/a refugee because home
                        is a tilled site of history.

                                    –

                tonight, i am the tallest of tidal waves & these
green hills call my sister's body
                        a hypothesis. i translate my wounds back
into *Simba* & *his goons.*
                        into the schoolhouse. & into a room full of
mangled bones

                                    –

                        at night birds peck holes into the dark,
the way i have always wanted
                        to catch so much of this earth

on my gentle tongue: i boil a broth
of stars & wade through chest-high grass

—

with bones & bones   & bones still
bleaching in the sun –
which is to say there is a moon in me
that swamps & swamps.

Don Taylor
THE SURVEYOR

My life has been made of measuring: miles, furlongs, chains, perches, roods, and inches. My labours produced sketches, charts, drawings, and plans, mere facsimiles of the world; now folded and furled in my study, mute and tethered by fading ribbons of every hue. In my youth I took to heart the dictum of Protagoras, that presumptive Greek philosophe: 'Man is the measure of all things.' I drank deep, with the abandon of a drunkard, of such 'truths', drank deep, at what I took to be the luminous, crystal fount of Academe.

My studies completed, I entered my profession which propelled me to the vanguard of schemes of great moment across the Kingdom. My conviction was that the natural and social Sciences would explain all that was in the world, or could be in the world. How could it be otherwise?

But in that year of '77, forty years past now, in the reign of the old King George, an incident was to occur, in a quiet backwater of Stirlingshire, of which the telling may not well serve my repute among men of learning. I was to be brought, horribly, to doubt the sovereignty of the senses, and to know that truth may often lie in murky and obscure places.

I was commissioned to determine the course, between the east and west seas of Scotland, most advantageous for the siting of the Grand Canal, and had taken lodgings with a weaver's widow, Gall, in the village of Banton, Stirlingshire. The cottage was neat and trim, the thatch fresh, and the outlook fair, though the air in that part was damp and cold, the dells and heuchs holding mournful mists and vapours in the night, and oft until well into the day.

On the second morning of my sojourn, my toilette was interrupted by a knock on the door of my tiny chamber. It was the widow, with her son Gregor, come in response to my enquiry after an able lad to assist me with my survey. His mother propelled him into the room by means of a spindle applied to the small of his back, which instrument of torture appeared to be habitually attached to her left hand.

'Stand there Master Gall, if you will,' said I, to put the child, who was but twelve years old, at his ease. 'Hold my bowl and towel, while I shave. That's right, help me wipe clean the blade, thus and thus.'

At first I adjudged that the boy was slow-witted; at his mouth a constant drool of spit; his eyes, which were the most extraordinary blue – the colour of cornflowers – flitted in all directions within the tiny room. They took in everything, but avoided my gaze at all costs, as though I were the very devil.

'He is small, Mister Prentice, Sir, I grant you,' said the widow Gall. 'No scholar, but strong for his age, and will do your bidding promptly. Won't you, Gregor,' she said, causing him to slop my shaving water onto the rug by dint of again prodding him with the spindle. 'And he is especially noticing – which can be an advantage to your honour, if I may respectfully suggest, you being a Gentleman of Science.'

'What think you,' I enquired of the boy, dabbing cologne on my cheeks, 'to working on the grandest engineering project in the Kingdom? Hmm?'

'I think yon watter that you splash on your face, Sir, stinks like a carriage full of whores,' he replied without a moment's hesitation.

This elicited a crack on the head from the spindle.

And so, on account of the spirit he showed, I engaged him to aid me in my survey of the Kelvin Valley.

Gregor quickly mastered the simple tasks required of him, proving a cheerful and entertaining companion. One afternoon we paused for our simple lunch of oatcakes and crowdie, I resting upon a large horizontal antique slab that bore a Roman inscription.

'Begging your pardon Sir, but folks say you maun not sit atop that stane,' said Gregor, 'for that is the holy stane of the Romans, them that bigged the great wall in the ancient times.'

'Dead a thousand years, or more – the men that carved this memorial, Gregor,' I observed, burnishing a piece of apple from my waistcoat. 'Their cold stone will serve well enough as a table for the living. It is through our understanding that we honour the Ancients, not by submitting to irrationality. The enterprise in which we are engaged is the greatest and most progressive that this land has seen.' In my mind's eye I can see, even now, the smile of complacency that adorned my face. 'Men of education,' I continued in all my bravado, 'who are free from false belief, Gregor, will shape this world to our advantage.'

At that, as though to demonstrate his capacity for higher thought, my young companion leaped upon the aged curiosity, tucked his thumbs into his waistcoat, and addressed himself to me and the nearby flock of grazing sheep.

'Ah but Sir, the Meenister is fell opposed to the comin o the canal, ye ken.'

'Indeed? How know you that, young man?' I asked.

'Oh he has preached this very Sabbath agin the evil of the "Knaves of the Navigation" who will steal away oor watter . . . "and make the burns as dry as the desert of Zin; to slake the thirst of the canaal they will flood the holy ground, whaur oor blessed forefathers died bloody maaartyrs in defence of the Solemn League and Covenaaant . . ."'

'Desist, you blaspheming imp!' I called out, making as though to strike at him with my hat, but astonished by his comprehension and expression. Barely suppressing my mirth, I asked: 'What was the good Reverend's reason that the canal will injure the parish?'

'Oh reason he has, Sir,' responded Gregor.

'How so?'

Eyes closed, and drawn to his full height, which was but four and one half feet, hands raised as though in benediction, he resumed, in mimicry of the preacher:

'"Ken ye Bullet Knowe abune the Baanton Burn?"
'"Aye." Spake the folk as one. My good mither, mark you, Sir, the foremost amang the chorus.
'"Ken ye the Baaggage Knowe west o' the Lang Park?"
'"Aye, we ken," comes the response.
'"Ken ye Slaughter Howe, that lies below the Crowy Wood?"
'"Weel we ken," – a sigh of deep misery.
'"These be the blessed places," cries the holy man, "where lie the corruptible remains of sax thoosand slain saints. Nae man daurs disturb the souls of these dear maartyrs!"'

Gregor's voice rose to an impassioned crescendo and, falling to his knees, he flung wide his arms and looked to heaven; tears coursed down his cheeks. I entertained a suspicion that the boy, for all his supposed weakness of intellect, was intent on mocking me; but I held myself more than a match for this simple country soul.

I cast my gaze across the green mounds that lay scattered along the valley – the very picture of a verdant Arcadia. The wooded braes and parks rose canty enough up towards the rugged Campsie Fells that divided us from the fertile Carse of Stirling. But well I knew, from maps of a former time, that the scattered knolls were named for a terrible history.

'That here befell the Battle of Kilsyth, I know, a century since, on yonder slopes,' I responded in a tone that I meant to withhold approbation. I went on, 'but superstition needs must be vanquished. Our project will drive out ill-founded zealotry and bring peace and prosperity to the country.'

'Ay Sir. I ken that sleek ships will sail your new waterway, bigged on that hill. Though camels may not pass through the eye of a needle, oor tight-knit weaves will be freighted afar to grease the palms of the fine fat Glasgow merchants.'

'The benefit to the country, my young savant, is beyond all doubt,' said I, and bit into my apple.

As it fell out, that day, the fifteenth of August, which the Almanac named as the anniversary of the battle, my project was to survey the stretch of land known as Dullatur Bog: a dank and watery place, as might be imagined. At this place the valley became a plain of dun marsh grass, lying level between woody slopes. Here and there clusters of willow and alder crouched below the proud height of a solitary Scots pine. Atop the fir, the yellow eye of the fish-hawk assayed the monotonous flat where sedges rustled in the rising breeze. Through the afternoon, a cool mist, or haar, insinuated itself into the low hollow. Despite the gathering gloom, I determined to work on an hour more to complete our task.

On my instruction, Gregor advanced, until the measuring chain he bore was extended to its full length. At that he held erect the ranging rod upon which I then sighted with the Circumferentor. The rod, its shaft striped white and red, bore a linen flag. Young Gregor formed the opinion that a white flag was not easily distinguished from the grey of the encroaching fog. Pulling a blue riband from his pocket, he wrapped it around the apex of the rod, giving it the gay appearance of an old-fashioned dragoon's lance.

'Here is a token for the blue of the brave Covenanters who fought for our liberty, eh, Sir?' laughed Gregor. In that dreary place I gave thanks for his high spirits and lack of care. I determined that this should be the final sighting of the day and ordered the boy forward. Only a curlew's mournful cry, or the anxious bark of a roebuck broke the gloomy silence.

'Sir, must we carry on, the day?' whispered Gregor, cowering in close to my person, his fingers entwined in the cuffs of my coat. He seemed fearful of disturbing someone, or something, in that desert place. A worried look flashed across his sunny features. 'I hae an unco feeling that there be bogles here in the bog. There's something no canny hereabouts.'

'Wheesht boy! You are as foolish as your benighted kirkman,' I upbraided him. I confess that the boy's sense of foreboding had unsettled me, so I brooked no contradiction in commanding him forward to his fate.

'What's that din, Sir?' he called to me over his shoulder as he advanced.

I, hearing nothing, directed him: 'Onward!' – scarcely disguising my impatience.

At that portion of the bog, the ground swelled upward in a convex form that resembled nothing less than the bloated belly of a great beast; the surface wobbled and trembled beneath his feet like a curd atop the milk. Again Gregor gazed at me over his shoulder, his face the very picture of apprehension. But I, with a curt nod of the head, ordered him on. Three more steps, and the mist engulfed the boy as if he were a wraith.

'Sir, Sir!' His disembodied voice came back to me. 'Hark at the shouting, the clishing and the clashing. It hurts my ears. I am afeared, save me, Sir!'

'Stand fast, boy', I called, struggling to control the tremor in my voice. 'Stand fast, I say.'

It seemed an echo returned my cry, but in an accent not my own. 'Stand fast, boys!' it answered. I ascribed the distortion to some trick of the topography or the wind. Fearing that I had placed my servant in mortal danger, I myself moved to the spot where I estimated he had reached.

There I found the ranging rod upright, impaled in a tussock, but of Gregor there was no sign. To steady myself I gripped the pole with trembling fingers, and sensed a trace of human warmth where his hand had rested a few seconds since.

Suddenly, the silence was torn asunder by the most dreadful rush of a hot wind, bearing upon it the clamour of men and horses in extremity; the clatter of steel on steel, and the thrashing of frantic hooves in plashy pools and dubs. My senses were overwhelmed by this tumult, until, on an instant, the noises ceased.

A second's absolute silence. Then a whistle, as of a blade slicing the air, inches from my head. I heard a crack, hard by my right ear. The top section of the ranging rod fell at my feet, cut-clean, a hand's width above where my livid knuckles clung still to the remaining fragment.

To my shame, I turned and ran as fast as the treacherous ground permitted. Darkness invaded the marsh as I reached the firm track leading to my lodging. I persuaded myself that Gregor would have fled homewards, by a route unknown to me, he being well acquainted with the ground. Alas, he came not home that night. I resolved to instigate a search as first light crept weakly beneath the cottage door.

A dismal dawn found me on the bog. But never a trace of Gregor was there on the swamp. The severed pole still stood. Throughout the day the good folk of the district scoured surrounding deserted workings, sinks and pits, but to no avail.

*

A final circumstance relating to the case is deserving of record. It reveals not the truth of the boy's vanishing, but may perhaps be of interest to antiquarians.

On account of my unsettled nerves requiring me to take bed-rest, a colleague undertook the planned boring process in the very area where Gregor was last seen; a crew and engine being brought from Falkirk for that purpose. The boring tool struck an object. On withdrawing, there was attached to the bit, what appeared to be torn flesh. Its dark and leathery look cast doubt upon its pertaining to Gregor. Nevertheless, I was sent for; whether to act as a professional witness or on account of my association with the tragic event, I am not certain. I observed the proceedings perched on a forlorn willow stump.

A half-hour of digging confirmed that there was indeed a body below the turf; ropes were passed beneath the form, and a hoist rigged. I watched with horrible fascination as, inch by fearful inch, the object was winched up.

As the quag gave up its secret, the very earth seemed to utter forth the demented lamentations of a host of lost souls, borne on the stinking breath of a thousand graves. Dripping from the slimy mire, emerged the form of a trooper, fully armoured in the manner of the last century. Erect, he sat, astride a grey mare, breastplate besmirched with crusted mud and blood, sabre extended 'at the charge'. And there, fluttering in the fitful breeze, pricked on the sword-tip (stained, but with its hue still visible): a ribbon, as blue as Gregor's innocent young eyes.

Samantha Walton
THE TORCH

When the Torch passes over me, I lift the frozen fruit from the icebox and set it out to thaw. Nothing tastes quite like it used to, but even darkness can't kill the flavour of strawberries. They used to say that we eat with our eyes, but they don't say that anymore.

In the bed next door, Cal is sleeping, and I creep around slowly so as not to wake him. He has been working all day and came home with the groceries and a headache. I asked him to tell me about his work but he passed the shopping bag over and kissed me, silently. Then he walked away from me and into the darkness of our apartment's back room.

I run a knife through an onion, using my knuckles against the blade to guide me. Once it has been sliced into rough half-moons, I tip it into the big pot and listen to it sizzle on the hob. The knife is the same dull grey as the room, and I have to make its shape out by the slight glint of red along its sharpest edge. The whole room is a web of outlines, sketchy suggestions of physical forms. During the Torch's absence, I use touch, memory, and these little stylised lines to navigate. The tomatoes, the protein flakes, the corn. I stir it all into a mash that Cal will be able to eat in three deep, careless gulps, and then I season it with salt.

In the passway outside, children are playing with a ball which flares and strobes each time they throw it in the air. It seems to fly impossibly high, a firework of flashing greens and reds. It comes as high as my window, filling the whole front room with its glimmer of tiny coloured lights. I wonder if it can see as well as the Torch, and then I stop myself. I force myself to smile when the sparkling sequins light up my skin, glittering like the creatures that once lived in the dark oceans.

The Torch passes over again and I stand still and face into the light. Every little Revolution is a blessing, Mother used to tell me. Like being touched by a god better than men have ever imagined.

Who needs a god in the heavens when you can have one passing his great white hand over you ten times an hour, night and day? She would shudder as she said it, and I wondered if she liked the touch of the Torch on her skin, as some people do.

When Cal came for me, I was keen to get the ceremonies over as quickly as possible. Mother wanted things to be done properly, but she wanted me gone too. She kissed me on each cheek when I left and said, you can make your own future now. Our names were on the register and we were placed in a couple's apartment on the 19th Circle. It was a long walk away from home, in a circle I had never visited before, but when I got there I found the crescent-shaped apartment block the same as all the others. The front room with its huge bare window and its kitchen, the back room with its bed and clothes rail, and the doorless archway between the two, as open as a mouth. Every six minutes, the same brilliant wave of Torchlight passing over us. It was like I hadn't left at all.

Now that I am gone, I wonder if Mother has moved her bed into the front room to feel the light white on her skin, night and day. It's supposed to be a sign of devotion, but it's not compulsory yet.

I will eat three strawberries and then I will get ready to go to the gathering. I will take my soft clothleather bag and my book, which we will take turns to read out loud as the Torch passes over. It's wonderful how the writers have adapted to the new conditions, writing the short segments we can enjoy in the little bursts we have. Sometimes, a woman will joke that she has become used to reading in the half-light during its absence. We laugh as if we aren't worried she might be telling the truth.

I close the door of the apartment very slowly so as not to wake Cal. There's no lock, there is no need for one. The door settles softly in its frame.

On the way down to the street, I share the lift with two women from the floor above. They are chatting about their own gathering. These women are singers and are gossiping about the administrator

who reads the lines out for them, how her voice is cracking and
how they must find their own notes so as not to be led astray
by hers. I wonder why they don't learn the lines by heart so they
don't need to repeat each line after her. But then singing is the art
of group mimicry, and if they sang their parts from their own
memories, the humility of the ceremony would be lost.

We separate at the street door with some kind, trite words and
they head down the circle torchwise, while I walk inwards along
the passway. It is impossible to feel homesick in a city laid out like
a labyrinth. Not a maze – the purpose is to never be lost. It's more
like a web, with concentric circles of housing strung together by
radiating passways, all of them leading to the Torch.

The Torch is bright white but the streets are the same deep dull
red as the back room of the apartments, an effect I once found
vaguely erotic. I cringe at the memory now, how as a child pretending
to be asleep I would watch the red halo of my parents' bodies as
they performed. It wasn't compulsory to do it each night, but
Mother insisted, the little fanatic. When Cal and I make love, I
have to try very hard to associate myself with the sensations, to
convince myself that it is my own body experiencing his touch and
his movements, and my own self moving against him in return.

The passway is quiet tonight. All I can hear are the steps of
women heading to their various meetings. You can't exactly see
their shadows, but you know they're there by the bulk of them, the
dark shape of their dresses, the bundles of their baskets cutting
black holes in the crimson gloom. When the Torch comes around,
it's like the flash of a camera freezing us all into unlikely positions,
like criminals. We take our bearings and then carry on along our
paths, the colours and shapes of the city imprinted on our retinas
for a few, intoxicating moments.

I dart down the 12th Circle and follow the curve of the street,
looking for the sign of the 56th Passway. The apartment blocks
loom up, grey-red and angular, with black cut-out windows partially
illuminated by the red bulbs strung along the lines between each

street post. When the Torch passes I can see the mothers standing in their front rooms, wiping their countertops or stirring their pots. If the angle is just right, I can see right through to the men in the windowless back rooms. They are pulling off their shirts or standing naked, washing in the chlorinated water of the corner showers. Sometimes a man is sitting on his bed, watching his wife's back as she prepares his meal. This is what the Torch is meant for, but still, it feels wrong and exciting at the same time. It feels exciting because it feels wrong. It feels wrong because it is exciting.

I enjoy the twenty-minute walk I am trusted to take all by myself.

I don't know why I was assigned the book gathering. I don't much like this kind of reading, and I find the material uninspiring. Waiting for the next turn is so dull I must close my eyes and imagine myself in a different place, in a different body. I think of colours and changing patterns of light on surfaces whose textures morph and shift like flows of strange water. These are things I've never seen, but I've been told about them and dream about them, sometimes.

Some women in my group find the silent gaps in the reading meditative. Others work themselves into a frenzy, repeating the last lines aloud, over and over. The words hang about in the darkness, humming, gathering power. I want to prick the words with my sharp little nail and hear them pop, then see them flail and fall to the floor. Instead, I sit silently, picking at my cuticles and trying to close my ears to the gathering sound. I wonder if the writers write by Torchlight too, or if they have another arrangement.

Chiara is here tonight, and Aileen too. Chiara has been trying to have a child so has missed the last two gatherings. Sometimes it's easier to get to the men when they are just home from work, before they collapse into the half-light of the back room. That's a safe reason for missing the gathering, though really the childless wives are meant to leave them on their own for a while to wash and to rest. The nights are so long, there is time for the performance after our first sleep. They are more dreamy and loving then,

when they've recovered from the heat and the light of work,
which hangs around their bodies even in the cool shadows of
our beds.

Chiara looks satisfied, and I wonder if she pounced on him just
as he came in. Did she pull him into her on the countertop, then
rush out so she could make it to the gathering on time? I ask her
how she fares and she smiles and says, Right as light. I imagine
them in the white light of the front room, bare and triumphant
and thrilling in the public gaze of their devotion.

Aileen touches my arm then and I feel better at once. Something
about her touch is grounding, tender. When she asks me how I am,
I say, Hiding under a bushel, and she laughs through her nose.

We drink the bitter tea and talk for a while about our homes,
our husbands. The Torch revolves once, enough to light up our
faces so we can tell who is in health, who is suffering, without
needing to speak to one another about these difficult things.

After the half-light settles we take our seats in the circle and the
administrator reaches for her book. We reach for ours too and
open them at the point we left marked at the last meeting. I fondle
the pages with my fingers and unfurl the corner I folded down last
time. The book is supposed to be treated with respect, but I have
no marker to keep my place. I think it is a mark of respect to
treat the book like this, like it is my tool, but that is not the
way. It suggests that I think the book is mine, when really it
is everyone's.

The next time the Torch lights up the room, the administrator
reads the first phrase, and we follow along. Our fingers trace a line
under the words and our lips breathe, without sounding, them out.
I know how the reading will go already, we all do.

The first error was to hide in darkness.
The second to think that dark hid more than light.
The third to reject illumination.
The fourth to demand it.

And so on, and so on.

Between each sentence is the long absence with the feverish, whispered repetitions. I used to try to meditate on the words during the absence, I really did. I even repeated once, when I was younger, but at some point I gave up.

We have been taught to push thoughts out during the absences, to keep our minds sharpened like a flint.

During the absence, you must bring the light yourself.

But I prefer to wallow in my own darkness.

Aileen is sitting next to me very close, and when the Torch is absent she crosses her arms and slips her hand over to squeeze my elbow. She pulses her fingers and releases, pulses and releases, then begins to run her finger back and forth against the thin, rough skin and bone. I can't register her touch with a smile, not with the administrator sitting across from me, but I like the feel of her fingers. I feel like I am in my own body, that she is touching me by choice.

The second error was to think that dark hid more than light.

As the reading goes on, the book tells us about the coming of the Torch. The darkness spread and the people were left in the shadows, clutching at the ravaged crops and trying to find water. It's the same boring old story, but behind it there is another story, the one Father told me. I remember his oil-soaked hands, his talk of mechanics and the full, clear light he worked by in the factories. He would look up at the sky, amber-tinged, and tell me how you could once see stars. It was Mother who handed him in, in the end.

Sometimes the Torch becomes a searchlight, and sometimes it becomes a floodlight.

The night after Father left, Mother was deathly quiet. I expected her to wail, to tell me she'd been betrayed, anything to show that something had happened. But she lay there silent as a stone. I stayed awake watching her, observing the way the red glow lit up her profile, turning her into a child's drawing of herself. Father had told me about the dull bulbs they use to light the passways, how it is the same safelight used to light darkrooms, where photographs were once made. I wondered if I stared at Mother long enough I would burn that image of her face into my mind forever. Father told me that even safelights weren't safe indefinitely.

I've never seen a photograph. What would we do with them, when everything looks the same? Still, I'd like a way to remember Father, and Aileen too, perhaps. The way she slips her hand away just as the Torch passes is so skilful and thrilling, I'd like to have a picture of the calm, just face she pulls when the light is on her.

The third error was to reject illumination.

My line comes next and I savour it, letting the words grow in my mouth and glow and linger in the air. I love the repetitions when they follow the cadence of my own beautiful sentence. I wonder if this is the deep, tender feeling of purpose that the women are chasing when they become administrators, but that's enough to snip the little pleasure off at the bud for me completely.

The reading will go on for another hour, each woman taking her turn. The turn means we must focus, and those who repeat are proving their constant devotion. I wonder how it will work when the girls who aren't being taught to read are old enough to join us.

Now that my turn is over, I can let my mind wander. I have learnt to keep my face very still – we all have – to take these trips into and beyond ourselves. I don't even need to close my eyes. My finger traces the lines on the page. I mouth the words, a cut-out picture of devotion.

I will walk right down the 56th Passway, arm in arm with Aileen, all the way to the perimeter circle. When I look deep into the true black of the outer sphere, I won't feel any fear. Father told me there are people living out there. I want to believe him, though I can't quite let myself yet. My pupils will dilate as they try to take in the impossible, obliterating expanse of the darkness. I would like to be the kind of woman who could run into it, and look back to see the Torch as just a pinprick of light abandoned in the desert.

Aileen's fingers are tracing lines on my flesh again, and I take the risk of closing my eyes to focus on her touch. I think that I would like a photograph of the marks she is making on me, documented in the darkness of my eyelids and on the underside of my skin. She is writing a book on my body and I am her only reader.

We will have to make do with touch, memory, and the little stylised lines she is making to find our way out of here.

Sarah Ward
SMÅLAND

Rich was under house arrest. The kids had woken at five and by ten they were climbing the walls. Getting everyone dressed required such a monumental effort. He'd have to persuade Adam that they were going somewhere worth leaving the house for. When it came to putting his shoes on, he was a stubborn little bugger. Sometimes you just didn't have the energy to think up incentives. If only Rich could sleep at night, maybe the days would be less like torture.

Neve had been round most evenings before she left, under the pretext of seeing the kids, but really to check he was properly miserable before she left for London. *I'm going to put myself first for once.* Apparently, he hadn't picked up on the signs. She'd told him she was lonely, but he'd no idea that this was what she'd really meant.

Where do you want to go? he said to Adam. The swings?

The park would be wet today but what did it matter.

I want soft play, Adam said.

Emily bounced onto the sofa. Yes!

Rich had vowed never to set foot in soft play again after last time. The idea of an undisturbed coffee was great in theory, even if the entry fee cost what he had for the entire weekend. But as always, it had ended in disaster. Adam screaming from the depths of the frame because he couldn't take the noise and Rich crawling in on a rescue mission. But now Adam had set his mind on it, there was no way the park would be an option.

Rich was struck by a brainwave. How about Small Land?

IKEA could sell anything, even play to kids. And where else could you get free childcare? He'd get a quiet spot by the window so he didn't have to watch the perfect families shopping for matching bed linen and storage. Thank god for the generosity of the Swedes. Without it, he'd be screwed.

He approached Adam, keeping the shoes behind his back, and held up a Lego plane.

Neeow, said Rich, zooming the plane towards him. It's coming in to land. Show me the light.

He moved quickly while Adam turned the toy over to find the button. One shoe, two. He hustled Emily to the door then patted his pocket for keys. Shit. Since moving he could never keep track of them. It was all part of the fog that had descended over his life. He checked the hall table, the bedroom, various bags.

Emily, have you seen Daddy's keys?

Emily giggled, twirling in the hall to make her coat swing out. Rich took both her hands and looked her in the eye.

Have you?

By the door, Adam was clutching himself. You couldn't ask him about the toilet directly because he didn't like going. Or maybe it was the directness he didn't like. Either way.

Adam, have you seen Daddy's keys? He lifted Adam to the bathroom and sat him on the toilet. Rich crouched in front, the plane's wing lights blinding him as they flashed in his eyes.

Adam smiled for a moment, then realised where he was. No! He kicked Richard in the leg.

Richard held him fast and kept his voice steady. You need a pee-pee, he said. Show Daddy the plane coming in to land.

I don't need the toilet! Adam hurled the plane to the floor and it skidded into the bathroom door, breaking into pieces. A blue light flashed out from under the shelving unit. He jumped off the toilet and ran towards the unit, hobbled by the trousers and howling with rage.

Richard left him on the floor and went to get a spare change of clothes. At nursery, he went through several sets every day, even though he was nearly five now.

Just boys, said the nursery worker. She looked round to check none of the other staff were listening and gave Richard a wink. *Little bastards*, she mouthed. Don't take any crap.

How school was going to work, Rich had no idea. Adam couldn't sit on a chair for ten seconds, let alone a whole morning. He sighed, pausing in the doorway to remember what he was looking for. He had the clothes, the bag, why was he in the kitchen? Christ, I'm trying to leave the house: check the drawers.

He'd stopped listening to all the advice about Adam. People don't like to hear about things not working. His mother was the same about Neve. The one time he needed her to take his side.

It's natural after spending all those years with babies, she said. She must need something you're not giving her. Have a think about it.

But thinking hadn't been an option. Not once Neve had reappeared in a blissed-out stupor, no longer hearing his questions, going through the motions of living without really being present. He'd had to drag it out of her, even though he knew the answer.

Michael was one of those rakish men that women liked. Neve had known him since school. He'd been to their house any number of times, had dinner, stayed over. He always had a story about the latest girlfriend who hadn't worked out. He said he didn't believe in owning possessions but in Richard's opinion, he was a freeloader.

It never would've happened if you hadn't stopped noticing me, Neve said. I mean, do I exist? She pressed his hand and looked into his eyes. We're all going to die, Rich. Don't you see? I need a life.

Richard stared at her as she leaned against the sink in the kitchen, intimate companion and total stranger, and imagined himself as an underwater Houdini. It would go to the wire, but somehow, he would escape the box before his lungs gave up. Everyone went through this stuff. He didn't believe that she would actually walk out and leave the children. They were the trump card, the anchor.

He didn't have the chance to find whatever it was that needed noticing. A week later, she left on a business trip with Michael in tow. While Richard wiped another shitty bum, filled the washing machine before work and spent weekends crawling through the tunnels of Cheeky Charlie's.

The house was haunted by her ghost. The theme from *In the Night Garden* plinked around in his head. *The night is black, and the stars are bright, and the sea is dark and deep.* He curled round Emily in bed, her breath warm against his cheek, watching the light of late summer fade at the window. What sort of future there was, he couldn't imagine.

He'd taken up smoking, but not in front of the kids. It was his night-time treat, out of the kitchen window, and she couldn't say a thing about it. He could murder one now, but it would have to wait.

*

In the hallway, Emily had taken his wallet and was emptying the cards over the floor.

He snatched it back and swept up the cards. Last time she'd posted them through the floorboards and he only noticed when he was standing at the checkout with the shopping, a loyalty card for the coffee shop the sole remaining item in his wallet.

His phone was ringing. It would be Neve or his mother, so a miserable conversation he could do without. He turned it off and put it in his pocket. He'd take a sketchbook and do some drawing. Maybe get a piece of that Swedish cake made out of Dime bars. Although he wasn't eating much these days. When he got the thing in front of him, he found it turned his stomach. He picked up the pen he liked, the one which made clean lines on the paper, then lifted the bag. Inside, the door keys jangled. Christ almighty, he was the jailor after all.

He stuck his head around the bathroom door. Adam was lying on his front, trousers round his ankles, trying to piece together the broken plane. His yells had faded into uneven gasps. Rich knelt on the linoleum, avoiding the pool of urine that had found a route towards the wall and along under the radiator. He pulled

Adam onto his knee, peeled off the trousers and socks, and wiped him down.

Are you going to play in the ball pool? Rich pulled on clean pants. Or watch a movie?

Adam looked at Rich as though he'd never seen him before in his life. Then he started bawling as though his heart would break. He gasped between sobs. The other light is gone!

Richard stared at the uneven plane, then crawled across and felt underneath the shelving unit. Hair clips, several clumps of dust, a hairbrush (hers). Finally, thank god, the essential square of plastic. Adam fixed it easily, pressing the button to check it still worked. The light gleamed off his cheek. He could fix anything made of Lego. He looked Richard in the eye this time, clutching the toy to his chest.

Daddy, I love my plane, he said.

*

On the way to IKEA they passed the airport. Adam craned in his seat to see the planes lining up for take-off. That's where we went with Mummy, he said. Remember?

Where is Mum? said Emily.

Mum is in London, Richard said. Why?

Last time they'd landed here, they were still together. That was when he still thought they could work things out. They'd sat the kids on top of the suitcases and raced them through customs on the trolley. Nothing to declare.

*

When they arrived, Småland was full. He scribbled out the application forms with a blunt pencil while the kids roamed. He had twenty seconds, tops, before something went wrong. A security guard was already eyeing up the children as they pulled the leaves off a pot plant.

Anything we should know about your child?

Hates banana skins, he scribbled. His hand was getting cramp. *Can become physically sick if he sees one.* He was going to write, *but at other times is absolutely fine*, and thought better of it. He looked around to check no other parents were watching. He hadn't brushed their hair in days. Luckily there wasn't a mirror in sight. He slid the forms over the counter and took the ticket. Even the Swedes relied on paperwork to some degree.

He took them for lunch upstairs, where there were crayons, and a stack of cushions in the corner.

Emily squeezed into his lap. I'm not going to soft play, she said. I want to stay with you, Daddy.

But it'll be fun, he said. Much better than here. There are animals to play with, and a ball pit.

Neve hated IKEA. She wouldn't set foot in the place. That was because she had a choice. People with family money had it easy. He felt a surge of pleasure at not having to look across the table at her sour face. Once, at the checkout, she'd started shouting that it was an insult to human dignity shopping in this place. *We've got the same stuff as everyone else, we're Swedish clones!* People gaped at them from behind their loaded trollies.

He didn't mind it. I mean, if you had the money. But who had the money to spend on furniture? If you had any money, it was better to *do* something.

You should care more about your environment, she said. It upset her that he never wanted to put up bookshelves or buy quirky vases from the second-hand shop. He wasn't that kind of man. He looked at things and thought, but do you need it? And usually you didn't. Unless it was food or booze. Or records.

The coffee was scalding and seared his lip. He watched the children making a den amongst the cushions. Emily was Adam's only friend: he was lucky to have her. She was only three, but he learned more from her than anyone. She handed him the cushions as he ordered her about, happy that he was letting her join in for once.

He had been for a date with a woman from work. Denise. But it hadn't worked out. In fact, it couldn't have been worse. He met her during lunch break, hungover, having stayed up late watching a movie and finishing most of a bottle of whisky the night before. She picked at a salad and sipped mineral water, talking about her children's Kumon Maths programme. His cheese toastie had too much pickle in it, and he told her what a mistake it was to overdo the condiments. He could barely swallow in any case. He racked his brains for something to say and ended up talking about Neve. How much he trusted her opinions on art.

He laughed now at his incompetence. How sheltered he'd been, thinking that everyone was the same as him. But people had different values; they lied and they were selfish. Like his friend Jason, who called to say he would stop by for the evening. Richard was touched: you needed friends when you were single, and he'd never been that comfortable with mates popping in when Neve was at home. She liked people coming, but only people she invited.

Jason phoned half an hour after he was supposed to arrive. Rich was in the kitchen making a curry, the first time he'd cooked something other than fish fingers for weeks.

Sorry, mate, Jason said. Something's come up at work. Richard could hear the muffled sound of the pub in the background, the laughter and the chink of glasses.

No worries, he said. No problem, mate. Some other time.

He hadn't heard anything since. The worst of it was the creeping bitterness, the suspicion that everyone else was having a good time. He was too bloody old for all of this. He looked at his watch: five minutes till their slot.

The Småland play worker distracted Emily with the bubble machine. The tears still shone on her cheeks, but her mouth shaped into an o as she watched clouds of bubbles floating to the ceiling. The only benefit of being a man was that women took over. They felt it was their responsibility. With the exception of Neve, of course.

Richard nodded to the girl. Unspoken permission to leave, while the going was good. But the moment he turned from the desk, the novelty of an hour's coffee evaporated. His body felt so heavy he didn't even know if he could make it to the lift. He needed some air. Maybe a cigarette would do it. You weren't meant to leave the building, but where was the harm?

He emerged into the flat grey light of the car park. Trollies rattled past as people hurried to get out of the drizzle. He wandered round to the side entrance where the lorries were parked and shinned up the wall to have a smoke. He zipped his jacket against the weather. The chill felt good in his face and no-one was hanging off him, interrupting his train of thought.

Beyond the waste ground he saw the orange sock of the airfield dancing in the wind. The tobacco was going to his head. He stubbed the cigarette on a brick and jumped down into the scrub on the opposite side. The wind blasted across the wasteland, roughing up his hair and swirling rain into his eyes. He started to run, long strides through the grass. The air was cold, but his body warmed up fast. He peeled off the jacket as he ran, keeping his eye all the time on the windsock ahead. His thighs worked, pushing the ground away faster, flashes of earth and scrub jolting across his vision.

He heard the roar of the engine before the plane appeared below the clouds. It was straight ahead of him, wing lights illuminated as it came down slow. He knew the flight path, over the city then swinging wide above the loch and approaching from the west, down across the wet fields. Thick swathes of grass cut into his shins and the rain was coming down in sheets, plastering his hair so he could barely see. The plane veered out towards the mountains and disappeared into a cloud that muffled the sound.

A crow cawed from the telegraph wire on the arterial road. He counted the seconds with his swishing feet, heard the engines boom as the plane pitched and descended. It was gaining on him now. The noise had dropped but he could feel the power behind him.

He crashed through a hole in the fence and felt the shadow cover
him, the smooth belly and the wings spread, notched in for landing.
He made the runway, spread-eagled, his cheek against the tarmac.
He clung on as though he might fall off the earth and braced himself
for impact, the plane's wheels sending a shower of sparks into the
grey afternoon smirr.

Gillian Watson
DIGS

My new London boyfriend says he's actually from Slough, but I don't know what that means. Blurry corners of office blocks in mind. We meet online, he, WernhamHogg20, me, queen_street. My profile, an early-twenties relic dusted off for late-twenties consumption, leans heavily on my Glasgow upbringing. WernhamHogg20 can't get enough. *You're from Glasgow? That's cool. What's it like?* Great city. Amazing to go out in. *Really? Am heading soon, any recs?* . . . Well, I haven't actually been out there in years haha. Rumbled—

I live in a yellowing terraced house in East London that once belonged to an old lady. My housemates and I walk through her gated shower to get to the garden. In summer the slugs join us there. WernhamHogg20 lives with his family in Slough. We meet in what might be the middle, by the office building near King's Cross where he works. I told him I'd started drinking coffee, so he takes us to a smart place with a short menu, but they don't do iced with syrups and milk, which is the only way I know how to drink it, so I tell him *I just really want something fresh* and order a freshly squeezed orange juice. The cloudy liquid is like battery acid on my empty stomach but I smile and go *mmmmm*.

My new London boyfriend is more delicate than I guessed from his pictures, with a considered, actorly voice and thin white hands. His eyes close when he smiles, making little half-moon lines. We spend a while deciding where to go next for food. He stands pleasingly close to me while we look up restaurants on my phone. He smells of clean laundry and sweat. We pick a new Italian place in a former railway yard undergoing regeneration. He tells me about his family on the way to the restaurant. His mother is a cleaner in a local gym and his father fits fire doors. He still pays dig money. Sometimes they need it from him earlier, to cover unexpected bills and birthdays. I don't know what to say to this – I've never been the rich one before – so I reach around to touch his back. His shirt clings damp to my hand.

In the restaurant, we take our seats, order a jug of water, and pizzas. Any drinks for you? *The water's fine, thanks,* he says, and a lovely big sweating glass of Coke recedes sadly from my vision. When the pizzas come, his has a big egg wobbling in the middle of the mozzarella. He looks at me then the egg then back at me. He raises an eyebrow as he gives the yolk an inquiring tap with his fork. It breaks, and that's when I decide I love him.

*

I want to move out of the old lady's old house, so my London boyfriend and I move in together. We rent a flat from a couple we know. Elin and Dave are moving to Stockholm. Elin is Swedish, and they want to improve their work-life balance. They don't want to leave too many things behind, in case they get in our way, but we don't want to look poor enough to say, *leave it all.* We need the plates, we need the knives, we need the tins of chickpeas, because we're children still and we don't have any of these things ourselves.

It's a Saturday afternoon when we move in, sunny for late September. Elin is packing up the last of their things. 'We'll leave the coffee machine, if that's all right,' she says, gesturing to a machine on the worktop that's small and squat and silver. 'We'll pick it up when we're settled in Stockholm. Do you guys like coffee?'

I look over at my London boyfriend, my mouth a little nervous *o*. It's still frappé season in my chain cafés.

''Course we do,' he says quickly. 'How does this work, then?'

We watch Elin make us a bitter little espresso with the machine. It's hard to follow what she's doing. There are so many intricate little steps in the dance. I manage to get out of tasting the burnt brown liquid, slopping water down my sweaty chin as I sip from the lip of a carafe, claiming to be off caffeine.

When she takes the last of their things away in the Anyvan, we don't dare breathe at first. We leave the front door propped open, expecting her to come jingling back in, remembering a forgotten coat or yoga mat. In the kitchen, I keep gulping from the carafe. My London boyfriend uses the instructions to make his first proper espresso and sips it from the single Le Creuset cup they left. We're surrounded by boxes. My eyes dart greedily between them, looking for glimpses of the new white tile. When we realise the grown-ups aren't coming back, we let the door fall shut and start unpacking.

At bedtime, mostly unpacked, we drink coffee to celebrate. No-one is there to tell us not to. We stand in the kitchen talking until the early hours, marvelling at our good fortune under the LED spotlights.

'We can use that shelf over there for our spices,' I say, gesturing my cup full of sugar and milk at a space above my London boy-friend's head.

'And grow herbs on the sill. You're speaking my language.' He takes another cheery swig of black coffee from his big Sports Direct mug, unearthed from a box of utensils.

'Now that's why we're together,' I say. We clink cups.

'You know,' he says, 'I really can't believe our luck, living here.'

'Me either,' I say dreamily, stroking the brushed metal surface of the coffee machine.

When we go upstairs, my London boyfriend brushes his teeth and I take a proper look at our bedroom. There is a cupboard big enough to stand in, with a varnished wooden door, on what will be my side of the bed. The flat where I grew up had a cupboard like this in the hall where I would hide when I was little. I'd stand there among the coats, panting and slurping like a happy dog while I waited for my mother to come and find me.

When I hear my London boyfriend start to gargle, I pick my moment and climb in. When I click the wooden door shut, it stops just flush with my front. I am trying to catch my breath quiet when he comes back into the room. A moment's silence, then the fabric thump of him flopping onto the bed. I can't wait any more. I take a breath and crash through the wooden doors. 'Surprise!'

'Shit!' he yells, after a little pause. He isn't surprised at all. But he gamely rolls onto his front, face muffled in the duvet. 'I knew you were up to something!'

I splash onto the mattress beside him and he starts tickling me under my arms and chin. I giggle and whistle as I go rolling, a squeal spraying from my mouth. He reaches to hold me. I fold my legs around him and look at his big face smiling at me. It looks so kind I'm frightened. *I love you*, I say, burying my face into his neck to kiss the milky skin.

*

I let our new flat wash over my feet. The last time I bathed this often was when I was a teenager. The bathroom in my parents' flat was at the back of the building so the woodchip walls were always drenched in yellow artificial light. It was the only room with a door that locked, or even closed – the rest were so thickly coated with white gloss paint that they wouldn't shut. I would go to the bath and lie and stare, maybe read, the same old copy of a Point Horror that got fat in the edges with water. Alone in the locked room, I'd hear little creaks and breaths come and go outside. It seemed like my parents were always pacing. It was only after Mum had died and Dad would go to the shops that I would go for a bath and realise that the little noises were just the sighs of the house in the wind, and no one was there, had ever been there at all.

In this house now, in a forest touching Essex, the air blows through the windows, thrown open to the neighbourhood. The rooms are all the same white and grey, blending into one another, and when I have my baths I leave the door lying open; it could be nice, I think, if someone walked in. One day I find a little ladybird on the side of the tub, winking at me red and black.

Shuddering in the wind, this building has its own kind of creaks and breaths. Sometimes they lull me to sleep in the bath. I wake up in the new yellow light, head hurting from the hard ceramic, and imagine I can hear my mother calling to me through the open door.

*

In the mornings, our routine forms itself after a while: he stays in bed, I should have started working at six, I won't get warmed up until seven, he'll leave for work at half eight, nine, tissue at his nose for a nosebleed. *I don't need the doctor*, he says, rummaging in a heap of clothes for a clean pair of trousers. *I'm just run down.* When I get out of bed I go straight to the coffee machine.

I've decided I like coffee now. I like having to buy the beans, a new quiet aisle to visit in the supermarket of an afternoon, on my own except for the old ladies pulling their trollies around the corners. I especially like using the little cylindrical tool for tamping the coffee down, digging it down into the dark brown grounds until they almost seem to push back. I love the vigorous sound of the beans grinding, so thick and busy you could almost touch it, and the sharp warm smell wafting through the open doors. The sharp feeling of peeling the lid off a new jug of milk. I never used to buy milk, and now I share it with somebody else. I like bashing out the ice cubes on the worktop and slipping them in. Sometimes, when the ice won't come out, I bang the tray against the granite louder and louder to see if someone might hear.

It never tastes quite right, this coffee I make, it's never like it was in the first café where I drank from a tall glass and tasted every sip of coin-coloured syrup, but it's mine and I make it, and it's here, and as soon as I have it I can open my eyes. I'm ready to work, ready to answer the emails from Germany and Belgium, and every morning my London boyfriend comes downstairs, his scalp scaly and his nose red, and he looks at me drinking the iced coffee through gums that bled as I brushed, and he wishes me a good day and asks me if I'm going to go out, and I say *definitely – I mean, if I get the time.*

One day we try the milk steamer on the coffee machine. The booklet has long since fallen down the side of the cooker, so we find a YouTube tutorial. We discover the machine was designed by a celebrity chef and is worth a month's rent. I get over the surprise pretty quickly, but my London boyfriend can't let it go. *This isn't for me,* he keeps saying, *this is other people's.* He starts drinking instant. You're missing yourself, I laugh, as I pour in more beans. He shakes his head as he watches.

*

I find myself leaving the flat less and less often. There's lots to do around the house, and you can see the trees perfectly well through the windows.

My London boyfriend calls me every night on his way home from work. Tonight, I'm just out of the bath when he calls, and staring at myself in the bedroom mirror.

'Did you get out today?' he asks.

'Nah.'

'I thought you—'

'Too much work on. When are you back?'

'About an hour. D'you need anything?'

'Some milk would be good. I'll pay you back.'

'Mm.'

'So I was looking at the house today and I was thinking . . . What – would you think . . . about getting a cleaner?'

He doesn't say anything.

'It's just getting so dirty, and I don't have time . . . what do you think?'

I look down and grab my belly absent-mindedly as I wait for his answer. There are little red claw marks on my skin, like someone is trying to make their way out.

That night when he gets home, he makes me walk with him to the nearest high street. He uses the lure of a Tesco Express and its selection of treats. I don't like to go out alone with the wind whistling through the trees and the big spaces between them opening up like black mouths beside me. Cars go whipping past along the road but I can't be sure the drivers would spot a hand reaching out and pulling a girl into the darkness. My London boyfriend points out that the men in the woods are more likely to be interested in him, not me. I think about that when we go to bed, and he's fallen asleep again before I can touch him. I wonder if he's ever gone downstairs, out the back gate of the estate, and down the dirt path into the woods alone. It makes me feel restless. That version of him feels closer than the faraway outline under the grey bedsheets; I can feel its breath in my ear. I think about him coming home late with his shoes all muddy. I get up and go to the bedroom window to look at the woods, imagining his trembling white flank against the dark bark. The window would be a good place to watch from.

*

I am lying on the grey corner sofa with my knees bent up around my chest. We're out of washing powder so I'm wearing the last clean dress that fits, an old evening dress that's loose and swathes my extra belly. I am idly rolling an empty Coke bottle around on the sofa cushion between my feet and picking my fingernails.

'I'm going up in the bath,' says my London boyfriend from behind his phone. He's sitting at the other end.

'Nice! Do it.'

'Or will I run you one?'

I wipe a hand across my armpit without thinking, pretend not to sniff, don't need to, note the sour smell.

'Nah, I'm all right. I think I'll just read.'

He sits for a while, still scrolling. Sometimes I think it's girls, but when I catch a glimpse, I note with a little disappointment: Reddit again.

It looks like his fingernails might be dirty, but from this distance, I can't quite tell.

'What are you reading?' he remembers to ask. 'Is it work, or?'

'No, fun.'

'Oh?'

I'm reading a Japanese novel about a woman who leaves her partner and moves into a big flat at the top of an office block with her daughter. The cover is a lovely pale grey and I have shot it atop the sofa, maybe to Instagram, maybe to Tweet, or maybe just to fill up the SD card on my phone the way all my pictures seem to do now.

My London boyfriend is always asking me what I'm reading and I am always telling him too much and he is always picking up his phone about a third of the way through the description.

I stare down at my fingernails and let the sentences finish without me. The middle fingernail on my right hand is shapeless and fat, with a ballooning white tip, like a cartoon of a big fresh loaf. I make a little notch in the side and slice through it with the long nail on my opposite thumb. It creates a satisfyingly broad section of nail to throw away, almost as wide as what's left behind. While my London boyfriend scrolls, I casually reach my hand up to the back of the sofa and flick it away.

I do this all the time. I'll peel off long fingernails and flick or drop them behind the sofa. I picture our landlords coming back from Stockholm and finding a funeral of me when they clean behind it, piles of dried discarded life around the skirting boards.

Seeing a movement in the corner of my eye, I scan back to the triangular space framed by my folded-up thighs. My London boyfriend looks back. He's caught me in the surreptitious pick and flick. *Rumbled.* I giggle and pull a piece of hair across my mouth coquettishly, and he smiles flatly, wider and wider, something behind his smile stretching and drying into its own kind of grey and dead.

*

The lease is up soon. At night in bed, it's too hot to sleep with the covers, so we lie with the duvet bunched up between us like a little grassy verge.

'I was thinking we could get in touch and see about extending the lease already, you know, at least till they get back.'

He turns the soft lines of his body from me and burrows his head further into the pillow.

'—I mean, it would just be good to know, do you not think?'

It's a while before he answers.

'I don't know if I can live here anymore.'

'Okay, um,' I start. 'I thought you liked the flat?'

'It isn't the flat.'

In the room's tasteful grey, my tears sound like water gurgling through hot metal.

*

I wake up the next morning with my contact lenses still in and my eyes puffy from crying. For a few filmy moments I forget what happened, but as the room swims into view, the night before comes back like a bruise. I'm on my side of the bed, where I sat hunched and couldn't look at him, where I heard him say *I don't know who we are any more, who I am,* where I asked *don't you like living here with me?* and he said *it's not us any more, it's not me,* and cried, and I begged him just to wait another little while, to renew for six months, three, just till I'd worked out what to do next, where I said *I can fix this, I can't move, not again,* where I asked *why are you doing this to me?* and thumped the mattress and looked round to see his face, shapeless and sad. The side where I lay turned away from him with my feet touching the back of his legs, pleased he let me close to him, thinking it a second chance.

His side of the bed is empty now.

He's up early, I tell myself, he'll be downstairs. Maybe he's tucked up on the corner sofa watching a cookery show, or sleeping, the

soft lines of his eyes and mouth and his hips turned into smiles.
Maybe today we'll drink a cup of coffee together. It'll be like it
was before.

On the way down I stub my toe on corner of the bed. 'Ow!'
I say. 'Every time,' that way you do when you expect someone
to hear the sound and inquire. Descending the stairs I feel a
Tupperware silence, the absence of noise.

The sofa is a neat grey plain, and there's a note on the table.

Gone to Slough

I'm sorry

I re-read it a few times to make sure. I turn the paper over and
see the thick black letters stabbing back through the paper in
reverse. There isn't anything else.

I walk through to the kitchen. It's at the back of the flat, cool
and dark grey in the day. The livid yellow sunlight outside the
window looks like the glow from another planet. I look at it for a
minute and then I go over to the coffee machine and switch it
on. A little yellow card has sprung up into place, CLEAN ME.
The drip tray stinks when I pull it out. I take it over to the sink
beneath the window to look at it in the light. It's filled with thick
silty mounds of old grounds, little heaps of dead coffee half-
submerged in foul brown liquid. I drain the coffee water off and
look at the piles of dirt.

I prod one of the mounds of coffee grounds gently with my
pointing finger. It starts to disintegrate. Then I start rummaging,
scrabbling with all the fingers on that hand, then the other, until
I'm knuckle-deep in brown dirt. The coffee grounds are turned
like wet earth beneath my hands. *Maybe if I scrape down far enough,*
I think, *I'll get back to the start and I'll find it.* An old coin or a piece
of bone, a long weeping condom in the dirt. Before long, my nails
and my fingertips are caked in grainy specks of coffee, and the
tray's nearly bare. I stare at my hands for a while, but I don't see
anything new.

Maybe I won't ever find it, I think.

Then I start running water in the sink, hot, green, clean water. The sun is shifting in the sky, and the yellow light is starting to spill into the kitchen. I put the tray in the sink. The jet of water lifts the dark brown grounds from the tray and slowly sweeps them away. I watch the last of them circle round the plughole. Then I start scrubbing. Thing is, you need to get at these things quickly, so the dirt comes off.

Olga Wojtas
NOT MACHU PICCHU

Not Machu Picchu

A man is atop a ladder, fixing signs above the aisles. These include Jams & Marmalades, Milk, Crisps Nuts & Snacks, Soft Drinks Canned Drinks, and Household Cleaning. He finishes hanging the final sign, which reads Not Machu Picchu.

Not Machu Picchu

'So,' says the undertaker, 'any questions?'

'Yes,' says the work experience girl. 'What do you do when you've just got bits of a body? How do you stop them rolling around? And isn't it upsetting for the relatives if they've got a really light coffin?'

None of the work experiencers has ever shown such interest, insight or sensitivity. The undertaker beams.

'We learned a lot from the Second World War,' he says. 'All these people, sending railings, pots and pans for the war effort, when the metal was no use at all. So when they got Blitz victims, or the remnants of an air crew, they just bunged in some ballast. The rolling around was a bit of a problem, but we've overcome that thanks to my patented BodyBag.'

He opens the door to the preparation room. 'I hope your maths is up to scratch. You have to get the quantities exactly right.'

Not Machu Picchu

'Sir? Is this your briefcase?' The baggage scanner security guard approaches the suited visitor, who nods. 'There appears to be a padlock inside it, sir. I'm afraid we don't allow padlocks while the parliament is sitting, in case you padlock yourself to something.'

'I assure you,' says the suited visitor, 'I have no intention of padlocking myself to anything.'

'That's as may be, sir.' The baggage scanner security guard rummages in the briefcase and retrieves the padlock. Then she picks up a sheaf of forms. 'Your padlock will be waiting for you at the exit. If you'll just sign here.'

The suited man leans towards her but instead of signing here, he grabs the padlock, and fastens the security guard's charm bracelet to a metal ring on the baggage scanner. Since she is stuck at the far end of the scanner, no more baggage can get through.

'Undo your bracelet,' suggests the body scanner security guard.

'I can't!' the baggage scanner security guard wails. 'The clasp is jammed.'

Not Machu Picchu

The passengers have just finished an unappetising lunch, and are queuing for the unfeasibly tiny toilets, when an alarm begins to beep and the Fasten Seat Belts sign comes on. Another sign also comes on. It reads Not Machu Picchu. A stewardess faints.

Not Machu Picchu

Two youths wearing balaclavas and carrying pistols rush over to the supermarket checkout assistant.

'Give us all the money from the till,' snarls one.

The checkout assistant is wearing a badge saying *Happy To Help*. 'I would if I could,' he says. 'But I can't open the till unless you buy something.'

The other youth grabs a bag of sugar from a nearby shelf. The checkout assistant rings it up and the till opens.

The first youth grabs a plastic bag and starts shoving notes and coins into it.

'That's 69p for the sugar,' says the checkout assistant. 'And 5p for the bag.'

The youth hands over a pound coin and gets 26p change from the dwindling amount in the till. Then he and his accomplice run down the aisle marked Not Machu Picchu and disappear.

The manager, who has been hiding behind the tinned vegetables, rings 999 and asks for the police.

Not Machu Picchu

An aged farmer pauses and listens to the changed timbre of the aircraft engine. He pronounces on the basis of years of experience, and word quickly goes round the village that a plane is about to crash. The ladies of the village convene and begin knitting. They hold the vast knitted blanket taut as the plane plunges earthwards. The plane's downward trajectory is momentarily halted a few feet from the ground but cannot be prevented. The victims include most of the villagers. The aged farmer, who has decamped to a safe distance, is joined by the church warden who has been blown there by the blast.

'Knitting!' says the farmer and spits. 'Bloody nonsense.'

'Oh, I don't know,' wheezes the church warden. 'You've got to make an effort.'

'Why?' asks the farmer.

There is no reply.

Not Machu Picchu

The undertaker raps on the carapace with his knuckles. There is a satisfyingly dull echo.

'Very good,' he says. 'Excellent work. Lovely consistency.'

The work experience girl blushes with pleasure.

'Everything ready for the kiddies?' the undertaker asks.

The work experience girl looks round the visitors' room. 'I think so. I've set out crisps and nuts and soft drinks and felt-tips.'

The undertaker very slowly shakes his head. 'Felt-tips,' he repeats.

'Yes, felt-tips,' she falters and then realisation dawns. 'Oh.'

'What do we have in this BodyBag?' he asks.

'Bits of body,' she says. 'And a Le Creuset frying pan, casserole and gratin dish.'

'So?' he prompts. 'It's not a—?'

'It's not a cremation,' she says. 'The crem can't cope with Le Creuset. We use felt-tips for the crem. For a burial, we use nail varnish because it slows down decomposition.'

NOT MACHU PICCHU   171

She gathers up the felt-tip pens and puts them back in the stockroom, returning with an armful of nail varnish bottles.

The undertaker conceals his smile. She may have made a small mistake, but she'll learn from it. The girl is a natural.

Not Machu Picchu

The panda car screeches to a halt outside and two female officers come in.

The manager is trembling. 'They took all the takings,' he says.

'They paid for their shopping,' corrects the checkout assistant. 'And a bag. We still have a pound.' He is ignored.

'Where are they now?' asks the Woman Police Sergeant.

The manager points down the Not Machu Picchu aisle.

'A dead end,' says the WPS. 'We'll have this sorted in no time.'

'Be careful,' the manager warns. 'They've got pistols.'

'Water pistols,' elaborates the checkout assistant, but is ignored yet again.

The WPS and WPC run back to the panda car, put it in gear, switch on the siren and crash through the supermarket entrance, running over several deaf shoppers as the car careens towards the Not Machu Picchu aisle. The manager rings 999 and asks for an ambulance.

'Better getting an undertaker,' says the checkout assistant.

Not Machu Picchu

The undertaker is so inundated by requests that he has left the work experience girl to run the kiddies' party all by herself. He is confident she will rise to the occasion.

She has filled the kiddies with crisps, nuts and soft drinks and has now equipped them with the nail varnish bottles.

They approach the deceased and begin painting the carapace.

'That's lovely,' she says to one little boy, pointing at a crude oval of grey over a square of glittery navy.

The little boy carefully adds a blob of beige at the top of the grey blob. 'That's my dad,' he says. 'He was in a plane crash. That's him sitting on a cloud in heaven.'

'Lovely,' says the work experience girl. 'And that's your daddy in there?' She taps on the patented carapace.

The little boy nods proudly.

'How about writing a message?' the work experience girl suggests.

The little boy takes a bottle of coral nail varnish and writes in careful capitals: 'NOT MACHU PICCHU.'

Not Machu Picchu

'Sarge, look,' says the WPC. 'The satnav says *Not Machu Picchu* – we must be close.'

'Just park here,' the WPS orders. She switches off the siren, lifts the loudhailer and shouts: 'Come out with your hands up!'

'You'll never take us alive, copper!' one of the youths shouts back.

'Fine with me,' says the WPS, going to the boot and helping the WPC to unload the howitzer.

'Hang on, I was kidding,' shouts the youth.

The WPS lifts the loudhailer again. 'Sorry, I have to accept your first answer.'

She aims the howitzer. The WPC sifts through the subsequent debris for body parts, and finds a burst bag of sugar. On the bottom of the bag is a blue stamp, Not Made In Machu Picchu.

The WPC pours out the rest of the sugar, then takes the bag to the panda car and refills it with Class A drugs from the glove compartment.

'They were wrong 'uns, Sarge,' she says. 'We had to take them out.'

The WPS smiles. This girl is a natural.

Not Machu Picchu

With the baggage scanner security guard jamming the baggage scanner, visitors to the parliament still have to negotiate the body scanner, but are then free to pick up their unscanned holdalls, duffle bags, suitcases. Many of them have grievances and severe personality disorders.

A handyman is summoned to try to improve the situation. He has a hacksaw with him.

'Don't damage my bracelet,' warns the baggage scanner security guard.

'Don't worry, pet, I know what I'm doing,' says the handyman. With a few deft strokes of the hacksaw, he amputates her hand, and the charm bracelet dangles unharmed from the baggage scanner hook.

'That's it fixed,' the handyman calls to the body scanner security guard, but before the baggage scanner can be started up again, one of the crazies in the debating chamber's public gallery starts chucking around stick grenades, and the ceilings collapse.

Machu Picchu

A man is sitting on the ritual Inti Watana stone, kicking his heels. He is holding a placard which reads 'Nothing Is Happening Here.'

BIOGRAPHIES

Patricia Ace is the author of the poetry collections *First Blood* (HappenStance, 2006), *Fabulous Beast* (Freight Books, 2013), and *In Defiance of Short Days* (Fair Stranger Press, 2019). *The Lido at Night* is forthcoming from Red Squirrel Press in 2020. She lives in rural Perthshire and works as a yoga teacher and therapist.

Arthur Allen is working towards a PhD in Creative Writing at the University of Edinburgh. His debut verse-novel, *The Nurseryman*, won the the Eyelands Book Awards Poetry Prize 2019. Arthur was selected by the Black Mountain Press to be in the *Sixty-Four Best Poets* of 2019.

Dean Atta's debut poetry collection, *I Am Nobody's Nigger*, was shortlisted for the Polari First Book Prize. His novel in verse, *The Black Flamingo*, won the 2020 Stonewall Book Award and was shortlisted for the CILIP Carnegie Medal, YA Book Prize and Jhalak Prize.

Evgenia Jen Baranova is an author from Russia. Her most recent poems have appeared *Poetry Northwest* (USA), *The Raw Art Review* (USA), *Persephone's Daughters* (USA), *Meow Meow Pow Pow Lit* (USA), *Panoplyzine* (USA), *Transcend: A Literary Magazine* (USA), *Triggerfish Critical Review* (USA).

Jack Bigglestone is a queer writer and reader. Originally from rural Shropshire, he now lives in Glasgow, where he is an editor of *From Glasgow to Saturn*. He was recently published in *We Were Always Here*, *Spam*, and *404 Ink Magazine*. For word-y things follow him on twitter **@JackBigglestone**.

Simon Brown (**@SKBwrites**) is originally from the Highlands but now lives in Edinburgh. He won a Scottish Book Trust New

Writers' Award in 2017 and his short fiction has appeared in a variety of magazines. He's currently working on a novel that involves death, cardboard cutouts, and people in hats.

Larry Butler teaches tai-chi in healthcare settings and facilitates writing for wellbeing groups at the Maggie Cancer Care Centre; publications include *Butterfly Bones* (Two Ravens) and *Arts on Prescription* (feasibility research paper for the Greater Glasgow Health Board). Larry edits books and pamphlets for PlaySpace Publications.

Angela T. Carr is a poet and creative writing facilitator. Winner of the iYeats International Poetry Competition 2019 and The Poetry Business 2018 Laureate's Prize, her work has been placed or short-listed in over forty national and international competitions and is widely published. Originally from Glasgow, she lives in Dublin. **www.adreamingskin.com**

Krishan Coupland is a graduate from the University of East Anglia MA Creative Writing programme. He has won the Manchester Fiction Prize, and the Bare Fiction Prize. He runs and edits *Neon Literary Magazine*. He is unduly preoccupied with theme parks. His website is **www.krishancoupland.co.uk**.

Carol Farrelly is currently working on a novel and short-story collection. Her stories have been widely published in journals, broadcast on BBC Radio 4, and shortlisted for the Society of Authors' ALCS Tom-Gallon Award and the Bridport Prize. She's a previous Jerwood/Arvon mentee and a Robert Louis Stevenson Fellow.

Alan Gillespie is a teacher and a writer from Glasgow with a debut novel due out in May 2021.

Originally from Glasgow, **Jennifer Harvey** now lives and works in Amsterdam. She is the author of three novels: *Someone Else's Daughter* (Bookouture, June 2020), *The Homecoming* (Bookouture, October 2020), and a third title, forthcoming in May 2021. When not writing, she can be found wandering the Amsterdam canals, dreaming up new stories. **www.jenharvey.net**.

Lauren Ivers is a twenty-four-year-old Creative Writing MLitt student from Mauchline, East Ayrshire. She lives in Glasgow with her partner and their cat, and is happiest at home.

Russell Jones is an Edinburgh-based writer and editor. He has published six poetry collections (most recently, *cocoon*, from Tapsalteerie), edited three anthologies, and was the UK's First Pet Poet Laureate. He has a PhD in Creative Writing (Poetry) from the University of Edinburgh.

David Ross Linklater is a poet from Balintore, Easter Ross. His work has appeared in *Gutter*, *Glasgow Review of Books*, *DMQ Review* and *Ink, Sweat & Tears*, amongst others. His pamphlet *Black Box* was published with Speculative Books in 2018. He lives and writes in Glasgow. Twitter: **@DavidRossLinkla**

A guest curator for the Scottish Poetry Library, **Aoife Lyall** was awarded an Emerging Scottish Writer residency by Cove Park in 2020. Twice shortlisted for the Hennessy New Writing Awards, her poems have been widely published. Her debut collection *Mother, Nature* will be published by Bloodaxe Books in 2021.

Crìsdean MacIlleBhàin / Christopher Whyte is a poet, a novelist, and a translator. His sixth collection, *Ceum air cheum / Step By Step*, with translations by Niall O'Gallagher, was nominated for two national prizes in 2019. CLÀR has just published his seventh,

Gaelic-only collection, *Leanabachd a' cho-ghleusaiche* (Childhood of the Composer). A fifth book of translations from the Russian of Marina Tsvetaeva, *Youthful Verses*, also appeared this year, with Shearsman Books.

Robbie MacLeòid is a poet and songwriter who writes in Scottish Gaelic and English. His work has appeared in *Gutter*, *404 Ink*, and *STEALL*. In 2020, he was StAnza's poet-in-residence. Robbie researches and teaches at the University of Glasgow.

Donal McLaughlin is the author of *an allergic reaction to national anthems & other stories* (2009) and *beheading the virgin mary, and other stories* (2014). Shortlisted for the Best Translated Book Award (USA) in 2013, he was awarded the Max Geilinger Prize in 2015 for his translations of Swiss fiction.
www.donalmclaughlin.wordpress.com

Callum McSorley's short stories have appeared in *Gutter*, the *Glasgow Review of Books*, *Monstrous Regiment*, and *Shoreline of Infinity*, among others. He was shortlisted for *The Big Issue* Crime Writing Competition 2019 and his fantasy noir novel *Burying the Dragon* is available now from Möbius Books.

Susan Mansfield is a writer, journalist, poet and playwright. Her poetry has been published in *New Writing Scotland* and by StAnza Poetry Festival. She is a past winner of the Jack Clemo National Poetry Prize and edited the anthology *Catching the Light: Poems Inspired by the Paintings of Victoria Crowe*. Her alternative passion play, *On The Edge*, was performed in Edinburgh in 2015. She is art critic for *The Scotsman*.

With an MA in Creative Writing from the University of Glasgow, **Mina Moriarty** writes poetry on themes of gender, sexuality and race. Her poetry has been published in *From Glasgow To Saturn*, *Gutter*, *The Blue Nib* and *404 Ink*, and she was short-listed for the Bridport Poetry Prize 2019. Her forthcoming chapbook *Exile/Home* will be published by Marble Poetry in autumn 2020.

Siobhan Mulligan is a DFA Creative Writing student at the University of Glasgow, researching urban fantasy and the southern United States. She is one of the editors of *From Glasgow to Saturn* and has had poetry published in *BlueHouse* and *The New Southern Fugitives*. Find her on Twitter **@siobhanmull**.

Valerie Nieman is an award-winning author of four novels and three poetry collections to date. She currently teaches creative writing at North Carolina A&T State University and is working on a haibun narrative based on a month hiking solo in Scotland. **www.valnieman.com**

Jeda Pearl is a disabled Scottish–Jamaican writer and poet. Performances include StAnza, Event Horizon, Inky Fingers and Hidden Door. Awarded Cove Park's Emerging Writer Residency and Bridge Awards shortlist in 2019, her writing is published by Tapsalteerie, Black Lives Matter Mural Trail, TSS Publishing and Shoreline of Infinity. **@jedapearl**

Sharon Gunason Pottinger was born in Chicago but since 2005 has lived in the far north of Scotland. Her debut novel, *Returning: The Journey of Alexander Sinclair*, was published in 2015. Her work has appeared in *New Writing Scotland*, *Northwords Now*, and anthologies by Caithness Writers. **tinyurl.com/sharonspage**

Meghan Purvis's translation of *Beowulf* was published in 2013 and won the 2011 Times Stephen Spender Prize for literary translation.

Her poetry has appeared, among other places, in *Magma*, *The Rialto*, and *The Interpreter's House*. She is currently working on her first novel.

Martin Raymond is a PhD student at Stirling University – a practice-based project exploring place in fiction. He has a MLitt in Creative Writing from Stirling University. He works with composer Aileen Sweeny on pieces for solo voice and choir and was published in *New Writing Scotland 37*.

Lotte Mitchell Reford is a London-based poet, writer and editor. She holds an MFA from Virginia Tech, and an MLitt from the University of Glasgow. She has previously had work published in, among other places, *The Moth*, *SPAM*, *Cosmonauts Avenue* and *Hobart*, and has work upcoming in *Lighthouse* and *Crab Fat Magazine*.

Olive M. Ritch is this year's recipient of the Scottish Book Trust's Next Chapter Award. Her poems have been published in many literary magazines, anthologies and websites including *Poetry Review*, *Agenda*, *Gutter*, *New Writing Scotland*, *The Poetry Cure*, and *In Protest: 150 Poems for Human Rights*. Ritch's work has also been broadcast on Radio 4.

Daniel Shand is based in Edinburgh. His debut novel, *Fallow*, won the Betty Trask Prize and his second, *Crocodile*, was shortlisted for the Encore Prize for Best Second Novel. He teaches at Napier University.

Mark Ryan Smith lives in Shetland.

Kathrine Sowerby lives in Glasgow and is the author of story and poetry collections *The Spit, the Sound and the Nest* and *House*

However (Vagabond Voices). Her new book, *Tutu*, will be published by Dostoyevsky Wannabe in 2021.

Richard W. Strachan lives in Edinburgh. He has had fiction published in *Interzone, Gutter, The Lonely Crowd* and in many other magazines. He was shortlisted for the Dundee International Book Prize in 2016 and for the Manchester Fiction Prize in 2015, and won a New Writer's Award from the Scottish Book Trust in 2012.

Ojo Taiye is a young Nigerian poet who uses poetry as a handy tool to hide his frustration with the society. He also makes use of collage and sampling techniques.

Don Taylor lives in Central Scotland and spends much of his time in the Highlands. Short fiction work has been published in print and online in Germany, the UK and the US. Pushcart Prize Nomination (2018); Finalist, Chester B. Himes Memorial Short Fiction Prize (2019); long-listed The Short Story Award (2019).

Samantha Walton is a poet, publisher and academic. Her books include *The Living World: Nan Shepherd and Environmental Thought* (2021) and a collection of poems entitled *Self Heal* (2018). She co-edits Sad Press and is currently working on a non-fiction book exploring the connection between ecology and mental health.

Sarah Ward is a writer and social science researcher at the University of Glasgow. Her novel *Resurrection, Port Glasgow* won the Lucy Cavendish Fiction Prize in 2017, and was long-listed for the Caledonia Novel Award. She lives in Glasgow with her husband and three children.

Gillian Watson is a writer and translator working from French and German. She grew up in Glasgow and lives in east London. She will begin a Masters in Creative and Life Writing at Goldsmiths in London this year.

Olga Wojtas lives in Edinburgh where she attended James Gillespie's High School, the model for the Marcia Blaine School for Girls in Muriel Spark's *The Prime of Miss Jean Brodie*. Olga's *Miss Blaine's Prefect* series is published by Contraband. She has had more than forty short stories published in literary magazines and anthologies.